EFFECTIVE
PRESS

Exceptional voices, superior business results

www.effectivepress.us
Shelburne, Massachusetts

© 2014 Dr. Keith Kantor

Printed in the United States of America

ISBN-10: 0988316323
ISBN-13: 978-0-9883163-2-4

Standard Edition

Library of Congress Catalogue Number pending

Note on our food guide and nonfiction essays: Select, limited content herein may have been adapted from Wikipedia® such that text is available under educational fair use or Creative Commons Attribution-ShareAlike License. Wikipedia® is a registered trademark of the Wikimedia Foundation, Inc., a non-profit organization.

Back-cover photograph courtesy of Smart Business Magazine (www.sbnonline.com).

DEDICATION

t is our privilege to dedicate this book to America's real heroes: the men and women of our armed forces, our veterans, and our first responders. Without them risking their lives — often giving their lives — to defend America and all of her people, none of us would be free to accomplish all that we do, and attain all that we have. Thanks to these heroes we are free, and the greatest country in the world.

ACKNOWLEDGEMENTS

thank the following for their help in making this book possible and advancing our vision for a healthier, more prosperous America.

Green Box Foods (www.greenboxfoods.com), the country's leading nutritional wellness benefit platform. Backed by parents, teachers, health care providers, and some of America's largest and most progressive employers and institutions, Green Box Foods helps millions of families like yours and mine manage and prevent disease, and lead healthy, active, and rewarding lifestyles. Green Box Foods rushed to fund this book, demonstrating again how devoted its employees are to the health, fitness, and prosperity of the United States of America, starting with our nation's children. The company has been generous with research for the resources in this book — including recipes, exercises, and food safety tips all families will benefit from. I can't thank them enough.

My Gym Children's Fitness Centers (www.mygym.com), America's number-one child development and fitness center, has been central to the good health of millions of children since 1983. My Gym's extraordinary program and facility helps children 6 weeks through 13 years develop physically, cognitively, and emotionally. They have hundreds of locations in more than 30 countries offering structured, age-appropriate, weekly classes that incorporate music, dance, relays, games, special rides, gymnastics, sports, and more. Now, in partnering with Green Box Foods on nutrition, My Gym is helping the families of all its members work and play to their fullest potential. Their experts have been extremely helpful in developing this book, not least in vetting our recommended exercises for safety and effectiveness. We are fortunate — and grateful — to have them as our partner.

Peter Crouth, executive chef, for proposing such a fun book and supplying the initial sketches of these colorful characters. Pete heard me on the radio as I was giving an interview about my previous book, *What Matters: Leadership Lessons That Just Might Save America* (2012), and reached out to me to see what we might put into print together to help children and families. As soon as I spoke with him, and saw his initial concept, I knew we had to make this happen, and so we did. Pete also helped design the recipes and many of the food safety tips you'll find inside.

Dana Yarn, registered and licensed dietitian, and an exceptionally gifted certified trainer. As I write this, Dana's baby is due within weeks, and her glow is a lovely reminder of why this book matters. Dana works for my food companies and has been invaluable in shaping this book: I thank her for the food descriptions and exercises, and for her careful attention to the recipes, as she's the one who's made sure they meet our healthy living standards. Dana also helped with food safety tips, health tips, and other resources. Dana's care and expertise shine throughout.

It's my delight to thank Karen DeFiore Kantor, my wife of 38 years, for all her contributions to my happiness and our success, and the success of this latest book. Karen is a registered nurse and an artist, and helped to make sure every word and line in these pages speaks to our stringent health and safety standards. Karen worked closely with Pete's initial drawings and coordinated with our illustrator, Sarah Adam, who did an amazing job on the final characterization, inking, and coloring.

The All-Natural Food Council of North America (www.anfcna.com) and the Natural Products Association (www.infonpa.org), for sharing with me their vast archives of health and nutritional information. Their belief in a healthier America through healthy living and proper nutrition is informative, invaluable, and inspiring.

And thank you. As a parent or educator, you're doing the most important work of all.

Yours in good health,

Dr. Keith Kantor

ABOUT THE AUTHORS

DR. KEITH KANTOR is an owner, and the CEO, of Green Box Foods, Inc., a unique all-natural food and nutrition wellness company providing a platform focused on improving health, preventing and managing chronic disease, and reducing health care costs.

In 2011 Dr. Kantor led Green Box Foods to the forefront of healthy living in America, chairing a Blue Ribbon Advisory Panel on lowering costs in and repairing the national health care system. Dr. Kantor's team of bipartisan health care providers and business leaders uncovered $253 billion in uncontroversial savings achievable per year, and laid out a road map that, if followed, would save the health of tens of millions of Americans, and restore the national economy.

Dr. Kantor is a popular speaker and expert radio, television, magazine, and newspaper source on entrepreneurship, all-natural products, and healthy living. He also is a decorated Marine officer and proud supporter of our nation's military veterans and their families.

He earned his bachelor degrees, in chemistry and biology, from City College of New York; his MBA from Chapman University; his M.S., in nutritional science, from Kaplan University; his doctorate in business entrepreneurship from Ashley University; and his Ph.D., in nutritional science, and Sc.D., in naturopathic medicine, from Corllins University.

This is his third book, after *Millionaire's Handbook* (1979) and *What Matters: Leadership Values That Just Might Save America* (2012), also from Effective Press.

For more information, including reviews, awards, interviews, blog posts and other resources, visit www.drkeithkantor.com. While there, download Dr. Kantor's health and wellness app for iOS and Android.

PETER LAWRENCE CROUTH is an executive chef who has served families and business clientele through Hilton Hotels & Resorts, Marriott Hotels, and Howard Johnson. He assisted in catering for the executive board of directors for the Special Olympics World Games held in Connecticut in 1995, and worked as chef contractor for large corporations such as Aetna, Inc., IBM, MetLife, and Pratt & Whitney. He also has worked for a large catering company that served Yale University and the office of the mayor of New Haven, Conn.

Peter earned his associates degree in applied sciences, culinary arts, at Newbury College in Brookline, Mass., and first earned notice as a writer in 2010, when, combining holiday spirit and his Red Sox knowledge, he won the first Boston Red Sox "Jingle Your Way to Fenway" contest, representing the state of Connecticut.

Today a chef contractor for a large health care provider in Connecticut, he also is happily married to his beautiful wife of 14 years, Jo-Ellen.

DANA YARN is a holistic registered dietitian, ACE-certified personal trainer and fitness instructor, and Life Time Fitness–certified metabolic technician.

She attended the University of North Florida, where she ran cross-country and track and field, and earned her bachelor of science and health degree in nutrition. She completed her dietetic internship at Atlanta's Emory University Hospital.

In her work, Dana counsels clients on proper nutrition through holistic lifestyle modifications and clean-eating strategies. She believes nutrition is the best medicine to fuel and heal the body. She coordinates health and wellness events, performs nutrition consults for customers, and writes nutrition-related research articles for Service Foods, Inc.

An avid athlete, Dana competes in triathlons, including those with Ironman distances. With the birth of her daughter, Lily, and her son, Austin, she has embraced new challenges to her personal nutrition, exercise, and overall lifestyle, and reports becoming a mother has made her a better dietitian and more skilled in helping families stay on track for healthy, happy lives.

KAREN DeFIORE KANTOR is a registered nurse who has expanded her knowledge of health and nutrition working closely with professionals in the field. After studying nutrition at Kennesaw State University, she began coordinating health and wellness events in the Southeast United States, and consults privately on nutrition issues.

In her capacity as a nurse over many years, Karen has worked in schools, hospitals, and home health care settings.

She also is an artist, teaches at the non-profit Johns Creek (Ga.) Arts Center, and is passionate about helping children express themselves through art. Working from co-author Peter Crouth's original pen-and-ink drawings, Karen helped our illustrator give voice to this book's cast of colorful characters, where they all but leap off the page.

Karen and her husband, Dr. Keith Kantor, have two children: Kimberly and Ryan.

FOREWORD | DR. CARA WELCH

Leading a healthy lifestyle is one of the easiest ways by which consumers can take control of their overall health and well-being. Providing access to nutritional foods and natural products is an essential step, but it's not enough. We need to pair that access with a standard of living that supports this concept — including a complete diet, proper hydration, exercise, and rest. Educating the younger generation, and instilling these practices for the entire family, offers all of us the best chance for success.

I first met Dr. Keith Kantor several years ago when my trade group, the Natural Products Association, was looking to write a standard and definition for natural foods. I reached out to Keith to work on the natural meat and poultry section and was blown away by his passion and determination ... and his bad jokes! Keith is truly passionate about providing access to natural and healthy foods to consumers across the United States. He's also determined to educate as many of his customers, and potential customers, as possible.

I was delighted when Keith asked me to participate in this book. Part of NPA's mission is to ensure access to products that will maintain and improve consumers' health. I believe the *Green Box League of Nutritious Justice* fits right into our mission and sets the stage for the work we do every day to promote healthy living.

As a scientist, I appreciate Keith's approach to "everything in moderation" and "nutrition paired with exercise." He doesn't expect the perfect diet to be the solution for all health problems, and he doesn't restrict his recipes down to flavorless foods. Instead, he advocates for a broad approach to healthy living that incorporates full-fat foods and dessert into a balanced diet. He also explains that exercise needn't be viewed as a chore — it can be, and so often is, a great deal of fun. The most important part is to just get up and get moving.

As a mother, I am so grateful for Dr. Keith Kantor's desire to educate our youngest consumers and to get them started early on eating healthy and complete diets and exercising regularly. And the way he goes about it with this book is absolutely captivating. Creating superheroes to walk the kids through healthy recipes and stimulating exercises involves the entire family in imagining, creating, and "fighting for" a healthy lifestyle. While I'm not sure I need Beauregard Banana to convince my son to eat his breakfast, I think Pasquale Peppers and Solomon Spinach are going to be real heroes at dinnertime!

Thank you, Dr. Keith Kantor, and your team, for spreading the word on healthy living! I have a feeling this smart, fun, and lively book will inspire both new and veteran eaters to lead a more nutritious, active, and truly rewarding lifestyle.

Cara Welch, Ph.D.
Senior Vice President of Scientific and Regulatory Affairs
Natural Products Association
www.npainfo.org

THIS BOOK IS FOR YOU

You've come to the right place to get fit, food-smart, and healthy for life. This book is many things — a fun adventure for kids to explore, a toolbox of tips and tricks for parents and teachers, an exercise guide, a cookbook, a library of resources on getting the most out of your kitchen and local market, a collection of treats and surprises, and a call to action to make the best choices for your health at any age.

Ultimately this book is a gift. Even if you've paid for it, even if it was something somebody said was "good for you" to read — the equivalent of new socks for your birthday — this book is really and truly a gift from us to you, personally, as we know from speaking to thousands and thousands of different people every year that there's nothing more important than taking charge of your own health, and when kids are in the picture, setting a good example.

Live the way you want, to the best of your potential, without spending a minute having to deal with a painful, costly, chronic lifestyle disease such as obesity, type 2 diabetes, hypertension, or, perhaps, cancer.

This book helps you live the way you would want to if you could reinvent yourself, start fresh. What changes would you make, when you're really honest with yourself? This book is a gift.

We know you're busy. We've got families ourselves, and we know how challenging it can sometimes feel to make time to do what we all know we should do: get enough sleep, drink enough water, eat a variety of plant-based and lean-meat protein, and favor carbohydrates from low-sugar fruits and non-starchy vegetables like broccoli and spinach along with cucumbers and cauliflower.

(Avoid starchy carbohydrates like bread, rice, and potatoes as much as possible. Even though they are whole grains, they'll drive up blood sugars more than fruits and vegetables.)

Knute Trition: With you every step of the way!

But those really are the keys to living as nature intends — as your body simply requires because of the facts of biology — and there is time to make that happen. We'll show you how.

"Oh, but I don't like health food." Let me set your mind at ease. We're supposed to live large, discover new planets, build great cities, take great risks, and play amazing games. We're not for a minute suggesting we all need to live out among the field and forests eating "rabbit food" and whiling away the days. We're saying eat good, simple, delicious foods that power us up for work and play. We're saying eat well. Know the delicious, all-natural food your body really needs, not the processed filler some ad agency wants to convince you that you need because that's its job. There is a light-year of difference between real, all-natural food and junk food (Mark Twain observed a similar difference between lightning and a lightning bug). There are worlds of difference between wolfing something down because it's sweet and temporarily filling, and feeling full because you've eaten the rights foods that give you a genuine, lasting sense of strength, flexibility, and well-being.

If you go without the nutrients your cells hunger and thirst for, and fail to mix it up with a lot of fun physical activity, and push your body away from getting a proper night's sleep, well ... you'll have only yourself to blame if you wind up in the doctor's office treating symptoms and then standing in the prescription line.

Better to get it right the first time.

This book is a gift. Enjoy it. And enjoy being the real, active, happy you whom you were meant to be.

Who are we?

This book comes to you from Green Box Foods, a unique all-natural food and nutrition wellness company providing a platform focused on improving health, preventing and managing chronic disease, and reducing health care costs.

Our wellness platform provides the "missing link" for good health that no other wellness company possesses: nutritionally superior, USDA-certified, all-natural and organic food.

Participants are supported through our nutrition programs and network of registered dietitians, doctors, and trainers. Our Wellness Center offers additional easy-to-use online tracking tools and resources to inform, educate, and foster member engagement.

Green Box Foods completes client organizations' health and wellness plan by providing participants easy access to high-quality power food and information to enrich their lives.

So, then, isn't this just another sales pitch?

No. It's not. It's a gift.

Most of the people reading this book may never be Green Box customers, and that's fine. But they likely are Americans, and Green Box if nothing else exists to support America in its time of greatest need. This book exists to improve your health, personally, through all-natural food, nutritional education, fitness, and proper supplementation, which we think is helping to prevent disease and solve America's health care crisis.

Crisis? Yes. Our health care system is overburdened and failing. In our view, the government's attempt to help is further taxing the system and speeding up its demise.

So this book is a gift, a lot of fun, and a call to action.

Our population is aging, and health care now consumes $2 trillion per year. That figure, like Americans' waistlines, is growing. That is no coincidence; it's a simple fact of poor lifestyle decisions and a lack of food savvy from the schools on up driving up obesity rates, which drives up health and insurance costs.

What about the Affordable Care Act? In our view, and we're health care providers, business owners, and award-winning entrepreneurs, this approach, while well intentioned, will work against Americans' health. Bureaucrats will make your medical decisions, your appointments will be harder to set, you'll spend more time reading magazines in doctors' waiting rooms, and your time in your doctor's care will be all too brief and of lower quality than you deserve.

We don't really have a health care system in America; we have a disease and accident management system. Let's be honest: who goes to the doctor for anything but an accident, cold, flare-up of lifestyle disease symptoms, or the occasional checkup?

So what will we do? We'll return to the basics. We'll prevent diseases before they develop, and stay out of the broken system for as long as possible. That's the goal of this book.

Meet the League

In the pages of this book, we show how children and families can lead healthy lifestyles and prevent or properly manage disease, live a longer, more vital life, and we'll do it with the help of a league of superheroes we know and love: the Green Box League of Nutritious Justice, fighting its never-ending battle on behalf of healthy, happy kids, debuts in these pages. We hope you like it. The League is squaring off, of course, against the Legion of Unhealthy Injustice, headed by some real sinister forces.

You, and the children you care for, have a role in the fight, and we'll give you all the tools you need, in these pages and at www.greenboxfoods.com. By no means are you doing this alone: with us, you're fighting for your health, for your family's well-being and security, and to save America. And that makes you a hero in our book too.

Green Box Foods, Inc. and I are also excited to help lead the Presidential Active Lifestyle Award (PALA+), formerly the Presidential Challenge Award, and are proud to be a PALA+ Advocate. You and your kids will find out more about that in just a few moments along with the League, and it's very exciting. Don't forget to check out the League's posters and download a helpful app at www.drkeithkantor.com.

A parting thought: the Centers for Disease Control and Prevention (CDC) said in August of 2009 that if we follow four simple rules we'll eliminate, or at least mitigate, 80 percent of all major diseases:

- Don't smoke
- Eat an all-natural diet with lots of fruits and vegetables
- Keep your weight down to a BMI (Body Mass Index) below 30
- Exercise for three and a half hours per week

We're proud that we came out with these recommendations two years earlier, in 2007, and added to the list the need for proper hydration and sleep so we can close that gap from 80 percent to as near 100 percent as possible.

Please let us know what you think. We're all in this together.

Yours in good health,

Dr. Keith Kantor

ABOUT THE ILLUSTRATOR

SARAH ADAM creates whimsical illustrations, comics, and paintings from her studio in Vermont. She has worked with a variety of media, both digital and traditional, including watercolor, acrylic, pencils, and ink.

She has self-published several coloring and activity books, and completed commissions including children's book illustrations, covers for publications, and brochures and catalogs for local businesses and non-profit organizations.

In addition to illustration, Sarah has more than seven years of graphic design experience. Along with freelance projects, she has worked for a printing company and several print and Web publications, and is part of the graphics team at a Vermont food cooperative.

To see more examples of Sarah's work, visit her art page on Facebook or check out her online shops at www.madsahara.com.

ABOUT OUR CHARITABLE PARTNER,
CHILDREN'S MIRACLE NETWORK HOSPITALS

Since 1983, Children's Miracle Network Hospitals has raised more than $4.7 billion — most of it $1 at a time — for 170 children's hospitals across the United States and Canada, which, in turn, use the money where it's needed the most. These donations have gone to support research and training, purchase equipment, and pay for uncompensated care, all in support of the mission to save and improve the lives of as many children as possible.

Green Box Foods is proud to donate a portion of proceeds from the sale of this book to our charitable partner, Children's Miracle Network Hospitals. For more information, visit childrensmiraclenetworkhospitals.org and drkeithkantor.com.

The Secret Origin of the
Green Box League of Nutritious Justice

The tale that started it all: bravery, friendship, teamwork, and two universes to save! This is the heart of the Green Box League of Nutritious Justice. The adventure of your life starts on **page 3**!

Your Guide to Good Food

Perfect for kids and the grown-ups who love them, these handy files break out our cast of characters and bring your family's food choices to life as never before. Get the facts starting on **page 27**!

Power Up With Green Box Comics

Action! Mystery! Romance! (Not so much romance, but a little.) Twenty-six artful comics you can call your own make you a Green Box Foods hero like Knute Trition, Ed Yucation, and X. R. Cise. Collect them all starting on **page 63**!

How Your Family Can Eat Healthfully

We stuffed a whole library on healthy living into this book. From organic and all-natural foods to the skinny on salt, sugar, water, sleep, and the most common — and preventable — chronic lifestyle diseases, we've got the science covered. Find out more starting on **page 179**!

Recipes for Good Health

Whether you're hungry for breakfast, lunch, or dinner, or a perfect between-meals snack, dig in starting on **page 209**!

Exercises for Super Bodies

Good food, good friends, a head full of smarts ... Now pull it all together. X. R. Cise shows you how to work your body for fun and fitness. Perfect for all ages, and beginners on up. Listen to your body, and we'll meet you for a custom workout on **page 238**!

Safety, Health, and Meal Planning Tips

There's no substitute for common sense, but kitchen safety is so important, we want to arm you with these essential tips for getting more out of food preparation and your family's dining experience. Be safe, eat well, and enjoy on **page 248**!

PALA+

The program encourages all Americans (international participants are also eligible) to make being active part of their everyday lives. The President's Challenge is designed to help motivate participants to improve regardless of their activity and fitness level on **page 255**!

The Secret Origin *of the* Green Box League *of* Nutritious Justice

An American hero like none other, and a world hero to billions, Knute Trition could be any of us. Join Knute now in this, the secret origin of the Green Box League of Nutritious Justice, as he makes new friends; soars to new heights of health, fitness, and personal responsibility; and faces the challenge of a lifetime.

1

A true story

Wherever you're starting from, it's never too late to change for the best, that's what I always say.

I didn't invent that saying, of course. That's a quote from the greatest superhero who ever lived, Knute Trition.

I've got his poster in my room — autographed — and all his comic books.

He is far and away better than those other superheroes. You know those guys.

I love hearing and reading about all of Knute Trition's adventures. I learn something great about myself with each one. Everyone knows about the time he helped those astronauts get a good night's sleep so they'd be ready to blast off and explore the Sun. Then there's the time he rescued all those dragons from the evil princess. Oh, and the time he battled Sugar Shark and his underwater army of mad nibblers.

Most people like the story of how Knute Trition defended the Earth from Salty Snake and the Pretzel King. That's the one they made a movie about.

My favorite Knute Trition story is the one about how he got his powers and formed the Green Box League of Nutritious Justice and saved two whole Earths. And I'm telling you, it really happened. I was there.

2
Knute Trition

Before he was Knute Trition, movie star and comic book mega-star and all-around great guy, he was just a kid. An ordinary kid living in an ordinary family in an ordinary house in an ordinary town called Picnic Heights that's not far from here.

And that wasn't doing so well.

Games that used to be easy to play became difficult, and then too difficult. Fewer and fewer people sang cheerful songs. Hardly anyone leaped out of bed eager to run outside and climb trees, skip rope, or build forts with their friends. And no one knew why.

Fragrant breezes blew. Generous sunshine warmed. Cool running water gurgled by, and here and there rustling red orchards, perky green gardens, and busy farms thrived, though only a few people were heard remarking that the air smelled delicious and earthy.

"I don't feel well," the people of Picnic Heights complained in passing. "I can't explain it. I just feel worn down. I had tons of energy an hour ago, but now my tummy hurts. I'm cranky. I stayed home today. I'm not in the mood to do anything."

And it was true: a lot of people stayed home and weren't in the mood to do anything.

This was the case in the Trition household, too, where Knute's father, Tom, wasn't in the mood to help Knute fly a kite. Knute's mom, Petunia, wasn't in the mood to wear the nice outfits she used to wear, and painted fewer pictures than she used to paint. Knute's little brother, Goober, always seemed to be bouncing off the walls and couldn't pay attention. Everybody was concerned about Goober.

Breakfast was dry cereal. Lunch was a burger and fries, with a soda. Dinner was pizza, soda, chips, and ice cream. That once cheered Knute up, but it didn't lately.

One day after eating a half a bowl of cereal and brushing his teeth, Knute decided to do something he used to do with his father, but hadn't done much since Goober was born. He resolved to walk down his street, South Treadmill Street, and into town. He felt good about the decision to go out, but didn't know why.

He shrugged into his blue sweatpants and sweatshirt, put on his backpack, which had generally useful things in it, and waved goodbye to his mother, who was on the phone in the kitchen. "I don't know my provider ID," she said to the person on the other end of the line.

Outside, Knute stretched. He'd always liked stretching upon reaching the sidewalk. It filled his clothes with fresh air, he imagined.

Now he saw Mr. Pleasance, the mailman, struggling up to his mailbox and dabbing at his forehead with a handkerchief. The neighbor's little dog, Fang, yapped frantically at the mailman from behind a chain-link fence.

"Good morning, Knute," said Mr. Pleasance. "A real hot one today, huh?"

Knute thought it felt nice out, but didn't contradict the man.

"Let's see, let's see," Mr. Pleasance said, reaching into his bag. "Ah! Here's something for your mom and dad," he said, pulling some items out and handing them to Knute. They were bills.

"Thanks, Mr. Pleasance," Knute said, and stuffed the bills in the mailbox. He considered bringing them inside, but suspected that if he went back in, he'd wind up watching television.

Walking away, Mr. Pleasance said to no one in particular, "Busy day, busy day. Oh, if only my head didn't ache so."

Fang seemed about to shake himself to pieces with barking, then stopped, sneezed, and trotted off.

Knute ambled past his brick-red school, Picnic Unified Elementary, which was closed for the summer.

He walked past Antill Park, which seemed lonely with its quiet, still swings and slides.

He walked past a bunch of older kids sitting on a stoop and playing with handheld video games that beeped and flickered weakly. None of them spoke, looked up, or smiled.

Turning right, he climbed Slate Street and headed for his friend Ed's house, which was halfway up the hill. Ed Yucation was the smartest kid Knute knew. Maybe he would know why everyone was feeling so low.

The Yucation home was neat and blue, with sky-blue shutters, and gardened in purple asters, happy little sweet alyssum, magenta bee balm, lavender, yellow yarrow, and tall, heavy-headed sunflowers. The lot was further defined by a neat green lawn and white picket fence.

A straw welcome mat at the door read, "Welcome" in big, bold, black letters. A stout, gray reflector telescope on a tripod stood at attention on the porch, and was trained on a distant point up and over the hills to the west.

Just as Knute was about to knock on the door, it swung open, and Ed was there. His usually neat brown hair was a moppy mess, his yellow Oxford shirt was rumpled, and he seemed to have run a great distance to get to the door. His eyes were wide with excitement.

"Knute! Come in, come in! It's the most amazing thing! What if I'm right! What if I'm right! We've got to do something! Come in!"

And he pulled Knute in by his elbow, and closed the door.

3

Ed Yucation

As usual, the inside of Ed's house was fantastic. Strewn about on tables, couches, and taped on the walls around Knute were careful crayon drawings of butterflies, birds, bats, poodles, dinosaurs, turtles, tigers, octopi, eels, and elk. Construction paper continents and islands burst out with facts and color; painted papier mache canyons revealed their bones in cross section; a see-through volcano diorama appeared frozen in mid-eruption.

From the windowsills clear prisms fed rainbow streaks into the house, and black and white radiometer vanes, powered by light pressure alone, spun around their glass-globe spindles.

On the ceiling was something new: sheltering all rooms spread a painted night sky so deep and detailed that for a moment Knute thought the house had lost its roof. It was like being in a planetarium. Thousands of bright constellations and other delicate smudges were set against degrees of lush velvet black, suggesting vast energies and timeless depths, powerful even in the morning light.

On the wall framing the door to the kitchen were charts and graphs, and columns of numbers; many articles clipped from journals and magazines; recipes and photos of everything from pitchers of very-berry smoothies to roasted root vegetables to plates of turkey meatballs and spaghetti.

Knute got only a taste of this scenery as Ed all but dragged him toward his bedroom, which for very good reasons the Yucation family referred to as the laboratory.

They got to the laboratory door, which was closed. There was a dry-erase board stuck to it, with a black marker dangling from it by a string, and a little sign printed above it in Ed's neat hand: "What's on your mind?" Beneath that a grown-up had written, "How do dry-erase boards work?"

Knute thought that was funny, and started to ask about it, but Ed interrupted him.

"Before we go in, I have to ask you, Knute. Do you have an open mind?"

"A what?" said Knute.

"An open mind. What I'm about to show you might surprise you. If I'm right, if this checks out, what I'm about to show you changes everything we believe about our town — about the people who live, work, and play here, and what might lie beyond."

"Beyond what? What are you talking about?"

"Just this," said Ed. "We may not be ... alone."

And with that last word he looked up at the star-sky ceiling.

Knute looked up too. He didn't understand.

Ed held and released a breath, put his hand on the knob, and opened the laboratory door.

4

'It's us!'

Ed Yucation's parents had helped their son convert his bedroom into four areas for different activities:

There was a place for his bed and dresser, with a comfortable chair with a floor lamp, and a bookcase of fun books, ninja figures, and snap-together bricks that held together to look like a jet fighter. The bed was made; the blanket was green and marked off by regular white lines, like a football field.

There was a place for a simple bench under an open window, with closed cabinets containing binders, a microscope set and other gadgets, and a fairly large fossil collection arranged on long shelves. One shelf held tanks for shimmering fish, sleeping box turtles, and burrowing hamsters

There was a place for clay, papier mache and other art supplies. Out on a table were jars of yellow, red, blue, black, and white tempera paints, with their lids off. Knute loved the smell of tempera paint, and he knew Ed should close the jars soon or the paint might dry. There were brushes in a jar of water at a small sink.

Finally, there was a place that was a complete mess. It seemed there was a little bit of everything happening there, from clothes left on the floor, to game pieces scattered, and even a toy piano, paint-splattered and left on its side.

There was a closet, and also an open door

lead
wh
wa
K

there was a picture of Knute
a foodstuff. He was himse
The only difference w
wore a big yellow K
fit and happy.
"What do
picture sho
now "A
Ferg
Li

guessed were ba

"I didn't know you collected

But clearly these weren't baseball cards. They were pictures of ...

"Well, I won't beat around the bush," Ed said. "It's us."

"It's food," Knute corrected. "Fruits, vegetables, carbohydrates, and protein."

"Knute," Ed began, "I don't know how to tell you this, so I'll just jump right in. It's always best to face facts, isn't it? According to my observations — and some other data — this is you and me and everyone we know in all of Picnic Heights, maybe even all of the world. Just different versions of us!"

Knute took off his backpack and leafed through the pages. Each page contained four sleeves containing one illustration each, and each illustration was named for someone Knute and Ed knew from school or town. There was Adam Applebaum, but here named Adam Apple. This was Curtis Caulfield, but in Ed's book was Curtis Cauliflower. The resemblance was striking. Ed was an excellent illustrator.

"That is me!" Knute marveled. And indeed,

Trition, but not as
lf, in his blue sweats.
s that in the picture he
n his sweatshirt. He looked

es this mean, Ed?" Picture after
wed happy, active kids: Angel Avedon,
gel Avocado," playing hopscotch. Allie
son, or "Allie Asparagus," roller-skating.
tle Gary Glick, now "Gary Garlic," swinging
on a swing. Nobody uses the swings at the park
anymore. Nobody felt so great or wanted to play.

Ed was silent.

Knute turned pages, then stopped. In
the binder, among the pictures of the most
expressive, happy, active fruits, vegetables, and
more that Knute had ever seen, glowered pictures
of some sinister-looking creatures: a rattlesnake
with a saltshaker tail; a shark swimming in a sea
of candy; a mountain-blob cupcake.

Ed Yucation took in his ceiling with a sweep
of his hands. "These are the faces I see looking
back at me from … up there," he said. In a softer
voice, he added, "There's something else you
should know. Time's running out. Here, let me
show you."

Knute was studying the creatures in the
binder as Ed led him to the door leading to his
little porch, and again he thought he smelled
jasmine. Then he remembered why he had come
to Ed's house to begin with.

"Ed, have you noticed how out of shape and
miserable everybody has become?"

Now they were outside. Here was another,
larger, more powerful telescope than was outside
the front door. There was also a sofa, a table, and

an open laptop computer, all sheltered by a little
overhang. A fountain burbled on the lawn, and
carp flashed around it in a little pool.

"Knute," Ed began …

On a small black mat on the ground, sitting
cross-legged and with hands drawn together in
quiet, graceful mediation, was a beautiful young
lady.

Knute dropped his book.

5

X. R. Cise

The young lady opened her eyes.

"Hello," she said brightly, greeting
the boys. Then she stood in one fluid
motion, seemingly without effort.

Knute thought she was lovely.
She seemed to glow of an inner light. With clear,
brown eyes, nut-colored skin, curly black hair
kept out of her eyes by a purple headband, and
dressed in flattering blue tank top and pants not
unlike Knute's outfit, she seemed poised and
ready for anything.

"Knute," Ed said. "This is Xandra. Xandra,
this is Knute."

Ed pronounced it Sandra, the X like an S.

"Hello, Knute," Xandra said. "I'm pleased to
meet you. You dropped your book."

"What? Oh. Oh!" the boy said. "Yeah. I was,
um …"

"That's OK," Xandra said.

And the two bent down at the same time to pick it up, nearly bumping heads.

Xandra came up with the book first, and handed it to Knute, who wasn't used to feeling so confused. Who was she? Why was she here?

"What did you think of Ed's pictures? Can you help us?" she said.

"I don't ... I'm pleased to meet you too. What do you mean, help you?" Knute said.

Ed jumped in.

"X. R., I haven't had time to explain. Knute just got here."

"X. R."? Knute said. Now it was more confusing than before.

"Yes, that's me. My name is Xandra Risa Cise. X. R. Cise. Hello Mr. Trition," she said, and she held out her hand formally. Knute took it politely, and the two shook. Her hand felt warm in his. Something about jasmine. She was a few years older than he. Not many.

"Hello," Knute said.

Xandra moved into the bedroom. She found the water bottle she'd left on the lab bench, and took a sip.

"Well, it'll be dark soon. We don't have much time. Now that Knute's here, Ed, do you want to explain about the window?" Xandra said.

Something about her face was familiar. Knute quickly flipped through the binder. There she was: X. R. Cise, cheerfully lifting hand weights.

"Knute," Ed began thoughtfully. "Remember outside my room when I asked if you had an open mind? This is when you'll need it most."

"OK," Knute said.

"It turns out, or it appears to turn out — I could be wrong, but for now let's proceed as though I'm right and then we'll try to prove me wrong — Earth is under attack from ... from space monsters. The ones in the book. And only you can save us."

"Space monsters?"

"Well, sort of," Ed said. "I agree that wasn't very precise. What's happening — we think — is that there's another kind of space, or a dimension, or alternate universe that has copies of all of us in it — except that they're getting healthier, and we're getting sicker. Those creatures figure into it. There's a split somewhere, see, and unless we do something soon, well, this could be the end of everything."

Xandra turned to look outside. Then she said,

"It's already after noon, and the time we have to act is rapidly disappearing, like the space left between a closing window and the windowsill. Soon you won't be able to move between dimensions at all."

Knute waited for the punch line. There wasn't one. Both Ed and Xandra were searching his face for a reaction. A few moments passed in silence. Then Knute noticed Xandra was hovering about three inches off the floor, quite calmly, still watching him intently.

"Knute, we need you to save the world," she said softly.

Knute felt dizzy. Then he dropped the book again.

6

'My dad's in the hospital'

Ed followed Knute down the street. Knute was going home.

"Knute, wait up!" Ed said. Knute was fast. The pair made it down Slate Street, through the quiet village they shared, past the elementary school, and all the way to Knute's house.

"Look, Ed," Knute began. "I don't mind that you have that friend over and she likes your

pictures and that you're trying to mess with me about other dimensions and space monsters. That's all very interesting. But I saw her float! Nobody can do that."

"Well, Xandra does it, so I disagree that no one can," Ed said. "I agree that it's unusual. Furthermore ..." And Ed closed his eyes and slowed his breathing.

While he was doing that, Fang — alert as ever — ran up to the fence and gave three sharp yaps.

Now, supremely calm, Ed appeared to grow taller. An inch. Two inches. Three. Knute saw that he was hovering steadily above the sidewalk just as Xandra had done at Ed's laboratory.

Fang saw Ed levitate too, and didn't like it. He started barking like crazy.

"There, you see?" Ed said. "It's still unusual, but I can do it too! And so can you!"

Knute got down on his hands and knees and studied the space between Ed's sneakers and the sidewalk. It was empty. He was "standing" on air.

"Everybody's getting sicker and slower in Picnic Heights, maybe even over the world. You said something similar at my house. We have a chance to do something about it. Those creatures are here," Ed said.

Knute stood up. "Gottagogoodseeing-youlet'scatchuplater," he said, and hustled inside, leaving Ed to Fang's mercy. The dog leaped six inches off the grass with each bark. Ed floated back to the ground like a balloon. At that, Fang stopped barking, sneezed in satisfaction, and trotted off.

Ed approached Knute's door and knocked.

There was no answer.

"Knute, it's lunchtime. Can I at least come in

for something to eat?" Ed said. He was genuinely hungry, but he also knew Knute was a good friend and wouldn't refuse this request.

The door opened slowly. Knute was there. He looked pale.

"I'm sorry we surprised you so," Ed said. We wouldn't have asked — Xandra's being here is a secret — but the evidence is so strong that the health problem is real and you're the key to solving it."

Knute held up a sheet of lined yellow tablet paper that his mother had written on in neat script and taped to his door.

"My dad's in the hospital," Knute said. "My mom's with him. He wasn't feeling well, and he went to the doctor, and the doctor sent him right to the hospital. They think it's his heart. Goober's at my aunt's house."

"I'm sorry, Knute," Ed said.

The two friends went inside.

7

'We'll leave tonight'

Little in the house looked good to eat. There was leftover pizza that Knute thought would be tasty, but he knew it wouldn't hold him until dinner, and there were plenty of snacks in the snack drawer, but those were mostly Goober's. There were dirty dishes and pots and pans in the sink. Knute wasn't sure what to do. He was losing energy and focus. He poured them each a glass of water. He hadn't had any water lately, and it felt great going down.

"Your mom writes that if she's not home in a few hours, your aunt will pick you up, or you can stay at my house. She'll check on you soon to let you know how your dad is. I know my parents would love to have you stay over for as long as you need," Ed said.

"In your book ... your pictures. My dad's in there," Knute said. You've painted him as a happy tomato. 'Tom Tomato.' He's hiking. He's even got the same shirt, hiking staff, and green backpack my dad has," Knute said. "Dad used to love walking and hiking, but he hasn't done it in years. He used to take me along."

Ed put his hand on the larger boy's shoulder. "Your mom's with him. He'll be OK."

Knute seemed not to notice Ed's friendly gesture, and walked around the kitchen, idly poking into cupboards and the pantry. A lot of the packaging looked exciting, but what was inside struck him as flat and lifeless, adding to his general mood. He liked to read, and by force of habit skimmed the ingredients listed on the packaging, but couldn't pronounce the strange, chemical-sounding words.

"I've felt so helpless. I've known for so long that things weren't right. Dad's loud snoring, gaining weight, always being tired. Mom's irritability. Goober's ... Goobering. Nobody's acting the way they used to. Nothing's the way it should be. I don't know what to do about it," he said.

"If there's anything I can do to help," Ed said softly.

"There is one thing. What did you mean about 'looking up' and seeing healthy copies of everyone in Picnic Heights? Can we really get there and do something to help the people here?"

"Xandra comes from that world. She says we can," Ed said.

"Is it too late to go?"

"No. I don't think so. The window closes tomorrow morning, though."

"How would we get there? What about these monsters you saw and painted? Are they real?"

"They're real. And they're here, all-around us. Xandra says she knows their names and how to fight them."

"Why are you two saying I'm the key to this? What does Knute Trition have to do with saving the world?"

Ed shrugged. "Xandra says all good things begin with one person, or a small group of people, making a strong decision, and acting on it. She believes that's us. She was very clear with me about that. 'X. R. Cise, Ed Yucation, and Knute Trition are going to save the world.' That's the first thing she said to me."

"Isn't it best just to call in the Marines?" Knute said.

Ed thought it over. "Your dad's in the hospital. This looks like a job for Knute Trition and his friends," he said.

Knute took a breath, held it, and let it out slowly. Friends. He liked the sound of that.

"I have to check on my dad. And I'll tell my mom I'm staying with you. After that we can go. We'll leave tonight," he said.

8

'I can answer all your questions'

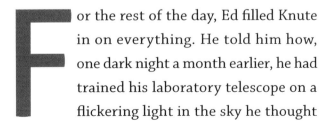

For the rest of the day, Ed filled Knute in on everything. He told him how, one dark night a month earlier, he had trained his laboratory telescope on a flickering light in the sky he thought might be the International Space Station. The station commander had been photographing cities, countries, rivers, and lakes in high resolution, and beaming the images down to a global audience. Ed wanted to turn the tables on him and paint his picture. Instead, what he saw was a mirror.

"Or a kind of mirror. Or a room full of mirrors," Ed said, "with each one showing a slightly different reflection. In one of them I was completely, utterly, me, looking 'down' in surprise."

"Is that where X. R. Cise is from?" Knute asked.

Ed shook his head. "She's from a different world she calls Cornucopia. We saw each other at the same time through our own telescopes. For the rest of the month I looked into their world and painted everything I could make out of the people there. They really do look like apples and spinach and football-playing livestock. I didn't see anybody who was sick or overtired or anything like that."

Presently the phone rang. It was Petunia Trition, Knute's mom. She was calling to say she'd be home late, and that she was glad Knute was to spend the night at Ed's house. Knute's dad, Tom, had had what the doctors thought was a heart attack, and that he was getting excellent care. Petunia didn't know when he'd be coming home. She said how much she loved Knute and was proud of him.

The boys continued their talk on their walk to Ed's house. A good thing they were going there anyway, Knute said, as he'd left his backpack there.

"So how did Xandra get here from Cornucopia? How can the both of you float like that?"

By then they'd reached Ed's side yard, at the carp fountain leading to his laboratory. Xandra was there.

"I can answer all your questions now. I wasn't sure we could manage three in the portal, but it looks stable," Xandra said. "We just have to be back by morning, or ... I don't know. We might be trapped there."

9

'What we need is a plan'

They were under the overhang just outside the laboratory. Xandra found a good spot without obstructions, and prepared to move her body in a way that she liked. She stood tall, spaced her feet hip-width apart, then lifted her arms out to the sides. Exhaling, she lifted her right knee and, keeping her back straight, touched it with her left elbow. She inhaled, returned to her starting position, then did the same thing but with her left knee and right elbow. She repeated the move slowly and gracefully a dozen times.

Then she took a few moments to rest. And

did it again. And again.

Through all this the boys didn't say a word.

When she was finished with her third set, she wrapped her arms around her body and pulled in for a nice stretch. Then she took a few sips of water from her ever-present bottle.

"OK. Thanks. That feels better," she said, smiling.

"That's ... that's OK," Knute said politely. "What do you call that?"

"What I just did? That's called a butterfly breath. Do you want to try?"

Xandra showed both boys how to do the butterfly breath, which they did awkwardly at first, but then picked up the groove.

"Very good," she said when they had each performed a dozen butterfly breaths. "Don't you guys exercise a couple of times a day usually?" she said.

"We used to in gym class once a day," Ed said, "but the school district cut gym from five hours a week down to one, so we don't have to. And anyway, it's summer."

"'Don't have to'? Xandra said, hardly believing him. "Moving your body so you feel good, challenge your muscles as you grow, and get better at being you isn't something you have to do, it's something you get to do. There's a big difference. Gym class or no gym class, exercising — really owning your body, enjoying how it moves and how you feel in your skin and clothes — is a joy!"

Ed blushed. She was right.

"There are a million ways to exercise," Xandra continued, now addressing Knute. "You can do things like I just did — there are so many ways

to gently move on nothing more complicated than a mat or patch of grass — or you can play a sport with friends or even just run and jump and tumble, and ride a bike. Anything that keeps you active, connected to everything you can do," she said.

"I like exercising," Knute said sheepishly.

"You do? That's great," Xandra said. "I thought so. You know how you can sort of look at a person and tell he's not interested in taking care of himself? The kind of person who doesn't even try, and keep trying even if it's hard at first? They're often not very happy or successful in other things, as they lack confidence and a sense of their own ability. But everyone can do something physical and feel great about it — if they'd only stick with it."

Xandra loved talking about movement. It was something she cared about and wanted to share about herself, and help other people find as a possibility within themselves. Knute liked that about her.

Ed interjected. "Well, as delightful as this is, butterfly breaths and bike rides aren't going to help us defeat these monsters and save the world," he said. "Now—"

"Don't jump to conclusions, Mr. Ed Yucation," Xandra fired back. "That's exactly how we're going to do it. Or, that's one of the ways," she said.

Ed crossed his arms. Then he realized he was being silly, and uncrossed them. Knute smiled at him reassuringly.

"You're quite correct. My apologies," Ed said. "What we need is a plan."

10

'Both worlds need help'

"Let's go in here," Xandra said, indicating the lab. She led them to Ed's long workbench, where she had a long roll of paper waiting. She pulled a stretch of paper out from the roll, found a purple marker, and on the paper drew two circles as large as grapefruits, about three feet apart. She named them Cornucopia and Earth.

"That's a nice name, 'Cornucopia,'" Knute said. "What are the people like?"

"Just like us," Ed answered. "From what Xandra says."

Xandra was still drawing. She drew a baseball-sized circle in between the first two, and wrote beneath it, "Portal."

"What's a portal?" Knute said.

"It's an opening that connects two places, like a door," Ed said.

"OK," Xandra said. "What's happened is that our two worlds have always been connected by a kind of cosmic string. We're practically the same world, really, just separated by the teeny-tiniest of infinities."

"That," Knute interrupted, "makes no sense."

"Well, hear her out," Ed said.

"You're good at describing it, Ed," Xandra prompted.

"OK," Ed began. He liked an audience. "The idea that we live in a universe that's part of a much more complex set of dimensions than we can see is pretty commonly accepted. That doesn't make it correct on its own, but it's certainly interesting to think about. What it suggests is that, if there is an infinite series of universes along neighboring dimensions, we might have a chance — if conditions are right — to reach through one universe to the next, and meet different versions of ourselves."

"Like through a door," Knute said.

Xandra was poised to write with her marker, but was enjoying watching the boys exercise their imaginations.

"Exactly," Ed said. "Now, I would think it would take tremendous energies to create such a door, or portal, if it's even possible, but we have one here that appears to be naturally occurring. I don't know. But the act of both Xandra and me, and all different versions of us, observing the same point of space with our telescopes, and seeing each other at the same moment, perhaps with the International Space Station nearby, it opened a window we could see through."

Knute looked to Xandra, who was nodding.

"And," she said, "we weren't the only ones who could see into other worlds. And we're not the first to travel between them."

"The monsters," Knute said.

"That's right." And, with a red marker now, she drew what looked like a large funnel with Earth at its mouth, the portal at its center, and Cornucopia at its spout.

"My people are getting healthier. Incredibly healthier," she said. "Just like you, Knute, as you've watched your world get sicker and slower, I've been alarmed and wishing there was something I could do to help. My people didn't start out as fruits and vegetables. We lived in moderation, took care of ourselves, got plenty of water, sleep, nutrition, exercise, and education — and then ..."

She stopped talking. This was difficult for her.

" ...And then we began turning into what Ed saw. These foods." She capped the pens. "People are starting to burst with energy. They play all day long. They're in more than great shape. I wouldn't have thought it possible, but they're overdoing a healthy lifestyle. If they were choosing to live this way, it would be one thing. But there's something directing all of this positive energy to my people against their will — and it's coming from your world."

Ed's head was lowered. He was sad, and considering the consequences.

"But ... My world is getting sicker. What does it mean?" Knute said.

Ed looked up and regarded them both. "It means someone or something is taking life energy away from the Earth — stealing it — and sending it to Cornucopia. And both worlds need help."

"That's right, " Xandra said. And then she tapped Ed's book of pictures. "We have the element of surprise. Ed saw the bad guys."

Ed nodded, turning to the pictures.

"Here they are, Knute. This is what we're up against," he said.

The names were as creepy as the faces looking up from the book: Cole Esterol, Di A. Betes, Hy Pertension, Salty Snake, Sugar Shark, and — most menacing of all — O.BC.D.

"What does O.BC.D. mean?" Knute said.

"Sound it out," Xandra answered. "The letters stand for Obesity Brings Children Down. Obesity thinks it's cute. These monsters were bad news before, but with Obesity getting stronger and calling the shots, they've joined forces and may soon be unstoppable."

"How do we fight them?" Knute asked.

Before anyone could answer, there was a knock at the door.

11

'You can finish playing later'

Ed opened the door, and his mom, Clara, was there with a dishtowel draped over her shoulder. She was an engineer, with long black hair, wide eyes, and a warm smile, and loved to cook. She entered, started to pick up Ed's dirty laundry from the floor, then thought better of it — and left it to lie there. Knute was worried what she would say when she saw Xandra in the room, but, turning, he saw Xandra wasn't there. He saw instead a blue marker at Xandra's sheet of paper, poised to write something.

"Dinner's in five minutes, boys," Clara said. And then she moved to hug Knute. "Your father's going to be OK, Knute. He's getting the best care money can buy." Knute was grateful for the hug. Then she gave Ed a frown. "I didn't know you had a maid all of a sudden. You know how to put your clothes in a hamper," she said.

"I know, Mom," Ed said.

Then she kissed her son on the cheek. "Five minutes. You can finish playing later." Then she turned, left the room, and closed the door behind her.

Knute whirled around — and there was Xandra, standing at the lab table, holding the blue marker and smiling innocently.

"How did you do that?" Knute demanded.

Xandra shrugged. "I exercised my powers of invisibility."

"You can do that?" Ed said.

"It's like anything else," Xandra said. "It just takes practice."

"Well, anyway, I'm starved. I haven't eaten all day, really. I need to stop," Knute said.

"OK. That's fine," said Xandra, capping the blue pen. "How about we meet back here after dinner and go from there. We have a lot of ground to cover," she said.

"But ... Aren't you staying for dinner?" Knute asked.

Ed agreed. "You're welcome to stay, of course. My mom ..."

"That's awfully nice, guys, but I can go home for dinner. I'll just step through the portal. It's not as hard as all that. That's how I got here," she said.

The boys walked her outside to the fountain area.

"Have a good dinner. Get lots of good energy. Healthy bodies, curious minds, and you can do anything," she said.

And then she smiled, slipped into a narrow sideways space — and disappeared.

12
Dinnertime

At the table were Ed, Knute, Clara, Ed's sister, Faith, who was home from college, and their father, Ben. Before them was a meal of spicy turkey and lettuce wraps, sides of sesame green beans, and glasses of cool water in tall tumblers. It was the Yucations' custom to observe a few moments of silence before eating, and then to dig in with lively conversation. Knute sat between Ed and Faith, and felt special.

"Thank you all for being here," Ben said. "I love when our home is full. And thank you, Clara and Faith, for pulling this beautiful meal together. It looks and smells delicious."

Clara smiled. "It was our pleasure. Now please, eat," she said.

"I'll help clear the table when we're done," Ed said.

"Me too," offered Knute.

While they served themselves, Knute looked around the kitchen. Unlike all the other rooms, this one was uncluttered in art projects and illustrations. Knute admired how clean, bright, and orderly the counter and stovetop were, and that the cookware had already been cleaned and stacked to dry.

"Except for the aroma of great cooking, it almost seems like you didn't even cook in here. Everything's so neat," Knute said to Clara.

"Thank you, Knute. We clean as we go. It's much easier to clean that way, and it frees us up to relax after meals."

He didn't say anything else for a few minutes. Soon he was busy eating his second turkey wrap.

Meanwhile, the Yucation family caught each other up on their day. Faith was going to the movies later with friends. Clara's firm had landed a big bridge design project, so she would be busy with blueprints and site visits for the next few weeks. Ben, the editor of the *Picnic Heights Herald* newspaper, was concerned about the news.

"We're running a story tomorrow about a health crisis in the country," Ben said. "Doctors have just declared obesity a disease. A full 36 percent of American adults and 17 percent of American children and adolescents suffer from it."

Ed's eyes widened, and he stopped eating.

"Obesity? What's that?" Knute said.

"Well, obesity is what doctors call it when a person has too much body fat. It leads to health problems such as coronary heart disease, diabetes, and damage to the back and knees, just to name a few. And obese children can find they're called bad names, are left out of games and teams, and often have a hard time finding friends," Ben explained.

"How do people get it?"

Ben took a sip of water. Then he said, "Well, if a child's parents are overweight, he or she might be overweight too, just because of their genes or the patterns the family has for eating and exercise. An unhealthy diet is a major cause of obesity. Fatty foods — or too much food, even if it's nutritious food — packs pounds on the body."

"Then there's exercise," Faith added. "That's what we're supposed to do to burn fat and keep the body working at its peak efficiency. I keep my weight down by exercising every day. I used to be too plump, and sometimes felt blah, but then I started going to the gym and practicing yoga. Now I feel great, have lots of energy, and have a lot of confidence to try new things."

Ben and Clara smiled at each other with pride. Their kids were on the right track.

"Great point, Faith," Ben said. "I've never known you to sit around for long. You don't spend hours and hours at the computer or watching television. I've seen you sit for maybe an hour at a time, then you're off to do something else. I like how you keep active and engaged."

"Thanks, Dad," Faith said. "Don't get me wrong, I like to sleep and relax, though ..."

"Oh, one has to have plenty of sleep," Clara agreed. "Eight or nine hours a night. Not getting enough sleep can actually make a person more likely to become obese."

Ed still looked startled. He ventured a question:

"What about hypertension?" he said to no one in particular.

Ben nodded. "Hypertension is a killer, no doubt. Hypertension, or high blood pressure, is a condition most often associated with adults. But kids can have high blood pressure too. That's when an unhealthy lifestyle — a bad diet including too much salt, excess weight, stress, and insufficient physical activity — lead to big problems for the heart, which is already working hard to pump blood through our bodies."

Clara looked sad. "Mrs. Springer next door takes medicine for hypertension. Her disease actually progressed to the point where she developed problems with her kidneys, which have a big job to do in the body in carrying toxins out of the blood. She's lucky she didn't develop problems with her brain and eyes too. Some people with high blood pressure do," she said.

Knute listened closely. He was interested to know that he wasn't the only one noticing a problem with his neighbors' health.

Ed spoke again. "What about diabetes and cholesterol?"

Ben took another bite of his meal, and nodded as he swallowed.

"You're asking the right guy. I know all about this. Diabetes is a chronic condition that affects the way one's body metabolizes sugar, in the form of glucose: that's the body's main source of fuel," he said. "With type 2 diabetes, the most common type by far, 90 percent of the cases, the body either resists the effects of insulin — that's a hormone that regulates the movement of sugar into your cells — or doesn't produce enough insulin to maintain a normal glucose level."

"Grandma Mercy has type 2 diabetes," Faith said.

That's right," acknowledged Ben. "She knows she did it to herself, too, with dietary choices that never let her insulin catch up to all the sugar she was consuming. I grew up seeing her suffer from it, and learned from her example, which

is why I eat as well as I do today, and insist you kids do too."

Clara smiled at that. She was proud of her family's health choices.

"Eating well controls diabetes?" Knute asked. This was news to him.

"Absolutely," said Ben. "It can, along with getting enough exercise. You see, our bodies are amazing creations, but part of the deal is that they need us to make smart choices to take care of them. In return, they take care of us."

There was silence for a moment.

"Grandma Mercy has to take injections of insulin for her diabetes," Faith said.

"She does," Ben agreed. "She doesn't like to have to, but she still isn't getting enough exercise, her doctor told me. There's plenty she can do to lose weight and get fitter, even at her age. I hope she turns the corner on this. She'll be touched to hear you kids are concerned."

Ed spoke: "Cholesterol is good though, right? I thought I read that it was."

Ben made a shaky "so-so" motion with his hand.

"There are good and bad kinds of cholesterol," he said. "We just ran a big feature on it in our newspaper's health section. We quoted a nutritionist who explained cholesterol is a waxy, fat-like substance made in the liver and other cells, and found in certain foods such as we get from animals, like dairy products, eggs, and fatty meat. This doesn't dissolve in the blood, and when you have too much of it — remember what I said about fatty foods? — it can slowly sludge up inside, and stiffen the inner walls of the arteries that feed the heart and brain."

Faith added an important point: "If cholesterol forms a clot and plugs up a narrowed artery, you could suffer a heart attack or stroke, and that can kill you … or leave you severely disabled."

Knute turned gray.

"I'm sorry, Knute," Ben said. "I wasn't going to say it, but Faith is right. It sounds like your father has high cholesterol. Surgery and medication are required, and he'll have to improve his diet and get more exercise as soon as he gets home," Ben said.

"I guess it's better not to eat all those fatty foods in the first place," Knute said quietly.

"That's true, son," Ben said. "I'm sure your father is aware of that now."

There was silence at the table.

13

A sweet idea

The rest of the meal passed in more pleasant conversation. Dessert turned out to be bowls of melon ices, which Clara had whipped up from cups of cubed ripe melon, unsweetened apple juice, lime juice, blueberries, and raspberries.

"No fat whatsoever, and it couldn't be more delicious," Ben said approvingly while spoons scraped the fruity ice.

"Thanks, love," Clara said. "I got the recipe from Green Box Foods."

"What's Green Box Foods?" Knute asked, as he and Ed were finishing their desserts.

"Green Box Foods," said Ben, "is the company that we get all our good food from. Mommy's work arranges with them to send us nothing but the best: nutritionally superior, United States Department of Agriculture–certified, all-natural and organic food."

To Clara, he added: "I wish my family had had this program when I was growing up. Through Green Box Foods and your job, we get access to nutrition programs and a network of registered dietitians, doctors, and trainers."

To the kids, he explained: "The idea is that a healthy worker is a happy worker, you know. Fewer sick days, less turnover, less expense."

Knute was fascinated.

"Mr. Yucation, is Green Box Foods good at fighting diabetes? And hypertension?"

Ed saw the light in Knute's eyes. He thought he'd figured out where his friend was going with this.

Ben smiled. "Yes, absolutely. And most importantly, obesity." Then Ben had an idea. "Wait, if you're interested, let me give you something …" And here he dashed off to the living room to look inside his computer bag. The boys and Faith left their napkins and empty bowls on the table and followed him.

"Here. I was going to show this to you over the weekend, but there's no time like the present," Ben said, pulling a brochure from a folder.

"Presidential Active Lifestyle Award," Ed began reading. "Sign up for the Presidential Active Lifestyle Award (PALA+) challenge today, and in six short weeks you'll be more active, making better food choices, and feeling great! Plus, you can earn an award."

"What do you think?" Ben said.

"Oh, I heard about this on campus," Faith interjected. "Adults can do it, but it's really great for kids. For kids, and teens, all you have to do is meet a daily activity goal of 60 minutes of physical activity a day, at least five days a week, for six out of eight weeks."

"That's right," Ben confirmed. "As an alternative, you can count your daily activity steps using a pedometer, a little gizmo that counts steps you take. Faith's goal would be 11,000 steps; the boys' goal would be 13,000. And each week you'd focus on a healthy-eating goal."

Knute read from the form Ed was reading: "There are eight goals to choose from, and each week you'll add a new goal while continuing with your previous goals. By the end of the six weeks, you'll be on your way to a healthier lifestyle," he said.

Clara had cleared the table and washed and dried the dessert bowls, and joined the family in the living room.

"What happened to the help I was supposed to get cleaning up in there?" she asked. "All of a sudden the party moved in here."

"Sorry, hon," Ben said with a smile. "I'm just excited about helping the kids go for this PALA+ award, if they want."

"That's a nice certificate," Ed said.

"I think we could clear off a little space on a wall for an award like that," Clara said. Maybe between the 'physics of football' poster and the cutaway anthill model."

Ed handed the document to Knute, who read the other side of the form. "This comes from Green Box Foods too," he said.

"Yep! Green Box Foods will help us stay on track to win, and they'll send us our certificate after we earn it. I'm doing it; who'll join me?" Ben asked.

Knute whispered to Ed: "I have an idea. I know how we can save the world — both of them."

14
Saving the day

The boys thanked Ben and Clara for dinner, said they would both try and earn the PALA+ award, which earned high-fives from Ben, and then dashed back to Ed's room with all the Green Box Foods materials. Xandra joined them a moment later with a gym bag slung over her shoulder.

"This is it. This is the key," Knute said.

"What is?" Xandra said. For the first time, she was the one who needed something explained to her.

"Green Box Foods," Ed began, looking in his supplies for a pedometer. "It's a company. They're used to fighting these creatures. Diabetes, hypertension, all the rest …"

"Obesity. That's the main guy we've got to stop. The others will wither away without him," Knute said.

"OK, but how?" Xandra said with a smile.

Now Knute was completely convinced. "Xandra, why did you tell Ed that only the three of us could beat these creatures?"

Xandra thought for a moment. Then she said:

"I believe the key to doing anything important is just to start. It doesn't have to be perfect. It doesn't have to have to be defended against people who'll say it won't work. It just has to be the result of a feeling deep down that you won't put up with things as they've been going. If you can change something for the best, and nobody else will — or can — step up and change it, then it's your job, sometimes, to be that person. And we call those people leaders. We need them."

Knute was silent.

Xandra continued: "I don't know that we can beat obesity alone, individually, or that anybody can for all time. We all need help to do anything big like this. I only know that obesity is killing my people, and yours — your poor father, in the hospital — and that somebody — we — needed to act."

Ed spoke now, having stowed workout gear and his water bottle into a small duffel bag: "I told Xandra I trusted you, that you're my best friend, and you're smart. And that was good enough for her; there was no debate. That's why you're here."

Knute was touched. He smiled, suddenly blushing.

"We can do this," Knute said. "We'll take the fight to obesity. And we won't be alone. Whoever you are, wherever you're starting from, it's never too late to change for the best."

He held out the PALA+ form and the other information from Green Box Foods.

"When we step through that portal," he said, "we'll be more than we are right now. We'll make a difference. We will not give up until we have beaten the enemy and kept our people safe."

Ed and Xandra listened to Knute with rapt attention. They knew this was history in the making.

"I'm in," said Xandra.

"I'm in too," said Ed.

Knute smiled. Now he spoke for them all:

"We say no to hypertension. We say no to high cholesterol. We reject the Sugar Shark. We will defeat Salty Snake. We will kick hypertension's butt. And both worlds will be free of obesity," he said.

Now they all put their right hands together, one on top of the other.

"We are Ed Yucation, X. R. Cise, and Knute Trition, and we ... are the Green Box League of Nutritious Justice," Knute said.

Suddenly all three felt tremendously powerful, and Knute realized they were hovering a good foot off the floor, and he felt he could fly or run or do anything. The way forward seemed quite clear to him.

"Let's do this," Xandra said.

"I knew you'd say that," Ed replied.

Outside, the portal between worlds opened, and the three friends disappeared into it with a flash, and went to work.

15

Your mission, should you choose to accept it

Did the League ever beat the forces of Obesity, which later went by the name the Legion of Unhealthy Injustice? Did Knute, Ed, and Xandra make it back home? Did Knute's dad recover, and has he started hiking again? Is Knute's brother, Goober, still bouncing off the walls? Did Ed and Faith earn their PALA+ awards? What movie did Faith see with her friends? What role did Knute and Ed's duplicates on Cornucopia play in fighting the Legion of Unhealthy Injustice? Is Fang still barking like a furry brown maniac somewhere in the night? Is it possible the heroes brushed their teeth and packed snacks before they left?

These are excellent questions.

I can tell you that the work the Green Box League began when they entered the portal, and brought the fight to obesity and its minions in the space between worlds, is ongoing. It's up to each of us to help by making ourselves more knowledgeable about what our bodies need and why, by getting plenty of regular sleep, by drinking enough water to keep our cells nourished, and by taking up a sport or other regular exercise.

The work goes on: with every action, the work goes on. It's always a matter of choice, yours and mine.

But how do I know all this? That's the question I hear all the time, when I tell this story: How do I know? Well, it's simple: I just do. After all, I'm a superhero too.

Just like you.

The adventure continues in the pages of the *Green Box League of Nutritious Justice* comics, to follow!

Your Guide *to* Good Food

You're not supposed to play with your food, but these foods want to play with you! Get up close and personal with our heroes and see why you and your family should make the stars of the Green Box League of Nutritious Justice household names. For more information on any of these foods, check out our recipe section and visit GreenBoxFoods.com.

ADAM APPLE.

Apples are easy to pluck from a tree or bowl, burst with flavor and nutrients, and are high in fiber in the form of pectin — and pectin helps prevent heart disease, lowers cholesterol, and reduces one's risk of stroke. Eating an apple just before you go out to play might help give you extra endurance, as it contains an antioxidant called quercetin that makes oxygen more available to the lungs.

SNACK FACTS

Apples come in all shades of reds, greens, and yellows, and are grown in all 50 states. Archeologists have found evidence that humans have been enjoying apples since at least 6,500 BC.

ALLIE ASPARAGUS.

With its tall, stout stem and feathery foliage, asparagus is a versatile vegetable indeed. Ninety-three percent water, it's low in calories and sodium, and crammed with antioxidant nutrients such as vitamin C, beta-carotene, vitamin E; the minerals zinc, manganese, and selenium; and needed protein and dietary fiber. It also contains saponins, which have been shown to yield anti-inflammatory and anti-cancer properties. Eating this special nutrient brings improved blood pressure, improved blood sugar regulation, and better control of blood fat levels.

SNACK FACTS

Onion-like asparagus was once classified in the lily family, but has since made a name for itself. It's also a spring vegetable, a flowering perennial, and when eaten can temporarily give urine a distinctive odor ... that only 22 percent of people can smell.

ANGEL AVOCADO.

Avocado, or alligator pear, refers to the fruit — botanically a large berry that contains a single seed — of the avocado tree. Green-skinned and fleshy, they may be pear-shaped, egg-shaped, or spherical. And their nutritional benefits seem endless. According to some health experts, it is one of the healthiest foods on the planet. We like them because they provide healthy fatty acids, which are anti-inflammatory and good for the brain. They're also a rich source of carotenoids such as beta-carotene, alpha-carotene, and lutein. Maybe best of all, due to their high fat content they're so filling they'll keep you from loading up on junk food, which you really, really don't need.

SNACK FACTS

Avocados play well with others! Adding them to salads or other vegetable-rich dishes will increase the absorption of their nutrients into your body's cells.

ARTIE ARTICHOKE.

The globe artichoke, a perennial plant native to the Mediterranean region, is a variety of a species of thistle cultivated as a food. You don't eat this straight as you would an apple; you have to take your time getting to know it. The leaves are often removed one at a time, and the fleshy base is eaten with hollandaise, vinegar, butter, mayonnaise, aioli, lemon juice, or other sauces. The fibrous upper part of each leaf is usually discarded. The "heart" (so yummy) is eaten when the inedible choke has been peeled away from the base and discarded. You can also eat the thin leaves covering the choke.

SNACK FACTS

Artichokes are a great source of fiber. One medium artichoke contains 10 grams of fiber, and several nutrients such as vitamin C, vitamin K, folate, magnesium, potassium and manganese. Keeping yourself supplied with these nutrients can keep you from getting sick.

BARRY BEET.

Beets are a unique source of phytonutrients called betalains. Betanin and vulgaxanthin are the two best-studied betalains from beets. Both have been shown to provide antioxidant, anti-inflammatory, and detoxification support. These colorful root vegetables contain powerful nutrient compounds that help protect against heart disease, birth defects, and certain cancers, especially colon cancer. They're also a great source of the antioxidants vitamin C and manganese.

SNACK FACT

*B*eets contain betaine, a chemical compound that relaxes the mind and in other forms is used to treat depression. They also contain trytophan, the essential amino acid found in chocolate and which contributes to a sense of well-being.

BEAUREGARD BANANA.

Usually elongated and curved, with soft flesh rich in starch covered with a rind that may be yellow, purple, or red when ripe, bananas are the fruits produced by several different kinds of large flowering banana plants. Plucked in clusters hanging from the top of the plant, bananas are a rich source of vitamin B-6, potassium, vitamin C, manganese, and fiber. As the average banana contains a whopping 467 mg of potassium and only 1 mg of sodium, a banana a day may help to prevent high blood pressure and protect against atherosclerosis. They are also a healthy snack that provides energy for long play or practice sessions.

SNACK FACTS

*B*anana leaves are large, flexible, and waterproof. Where they're grown they're often used as ecologically friendly, disposable food containers and plates. In some countries, bananas used for cooking may be called plantains.

BIANCA BROCCOLI.

Broccoli, a green plant in the cabbage family, has a large flower head that's used as a vegetable. The word broccoli, from the Italian plural of broccolo, refers to "the flowering top of a cabbage." Broccoli is usually boiled or steamed, but may be eaten raw and has become popular as a raw vegetable in hors d'œuvre trays. The leaves may also be eaten. We love it because it's got special cholesterol-lowering benefits due to its ability to bind to bile acids in the digestive tract, which helps get rid of cholesterol. Broccoli also is great at detoxifying the body for contaminants and hormones, helps keep vitamin D levels within normal ranges, and is anti-inflammatory — so it prevents cancer — and is a potent source of antioxidants, which keep you from getting sick or developing certain diseases.

SNACK FACTS

Broccoli is a man-made plant! It was derived from careful breeding of cultivated leafy cole crops in the Northern Mediterranean in about the sixth century BC. It became popular in the United States starting in the 1920s.

BLUEBERRY BILL.

This small, blue "superfood" repeatedly ranks as having one of the highest antioxidant capacities among all fruits, vegetables, spices, and seasonings in the American diet. Antioxidants fight off harmful free radicals, which could make us sick. Blueberries also help brain health and can even improve your memory. They're low on the glycemic index scale, so they won't make your blood sugars go up, which helps prevent type 2 diabetes and can help with depression. Aim to eat a cup of these sweet treats per day to get all of the benefits of their bounty.

SNACK FACTS

Off the bush, blueberries are sold fresh or processed as individually quick-frozen (IQF) fruit, purée, juice, or dried or infused berries, which in turn may be used in a variety of treats, such as jellies, jams, blueberry pies, muffins, snack foods, and cereals.

BOBBY BEAN.

Beans, also known as legumes, are a rich source of fiber and a decent source of vegetarian protein. Scientists find they're good at preventing certain cancers, particularly colon cancer. Their high fiber content also helps protect against heart disease. With these in your belly you'll feel full in no time, and in no mood to fill up on processed junk foods.

SNACK FACTS

*T*he word "bean" sometimes is used to refer to the seeds or pods of plants that are not in the bean family but nevertheless kind of look like them. For example, coffee beans, castor beans, and cocoa beans, which resemble bean seeds; and vanilla beans, which superficially resemble bean pods.

ALSO: Yes, they may make you fart. Enjoy the ride.

BRIAN BISON.

Bison are increasingly raised for meat and hides; the majority of American bison in the world are raised for human consumption. Bison meat is lower in fat and cholesterol, yet higher in protein than beef. It's also a great source of iron and folate, which keep mind and body working at their best. Classified as lean because it has less fat and cholesterol than most regular cuts of beef, it is a good source of many nutrients such as omega-3 fatty acids, vitamin E, iron and folate, which keep you and your brain healthy and strong. The antioxidants in buffalo keep you well.

SNACK FACTS

"*B*ison" is a Greek word meaning ox-like animal, while "buffalo" originated with the French fur trappers who called these massive beasts "bœufs," meaning ox or bullock. So both names, bison and buffalo, mean something similar.

SNACK FACTS

Higher-quality beef contains relatively more omega-3 fatty acids, which help reduce heart disease risk and inflammation. The other vitamins and minerals found in all-natural-grass-fed finished beef include B vitamins, selenium, zinc, choline, phosphorus, and iron.

BRUTUS BEEF.

Beef is the third most widely consumed meat in the world, accounting for about a quarter of meat production worldwide, after pork and poultry, making it one of the world's most nutrient-rich sources of animal protein. Certainly not every family eats beef, but those that do will be happy to know that all-natural and grass-fed finished beef is the most nutrient-dense kind you can get. Here's where you'll also find the most CLA (conjugated linoleic acid), which helps the body burn fat, boost the immune system, and fight inflammation — all-naturally. The five most popular cuts are chuck pot roast, best braised; top loin steak, such as New York strip or Kansas City steak; top round steak, flavorful and lean; top sirloin, great in a salad; and the big boss: T-bone steak, a great value and versatile as the day is long.

BUBBA BLACK-EYED PEA.

The common commercial black-eyed pea is called the California Blackeye, a pale-colored legume with a prominent black spot. Black-eyed peas are a great source of soluble fiber, which helps prevent type 2 diabetes and heart disease. Just one serving gives you a great amount of magnesium, calcium, and iron. These guys are a rich source of folate, which helps prevent anemia. Finally they're a rich source of antioxidants, vitamin A, and manganese, which help keep the immune system strong.

SNACK FACTS

In the Southern United States, eating black-eyed peas on New Year's Day is thought to bring prosperity in the new year. The "good luck" traditions of eating black-eyed peas at Rosh Hashanah, the Jewish New Year, are recorded in the Babylonian Talmud, compiled circa 500 AD. Today the black-eyed pea is famous as a widely used ingredient in various types of Southern cuisine.

CANDACE COCONUT.

Coconut can refer to the entire coconut palm, the seed, or the fruit, which botanically is a drupe, not a nut. (Now you know.) Found throughout the tropic and sub-tropic area, the coconut differs from any other fruits in that it contains a large quantity of "water." When immature it's known as tender-nut or jelly-nut, and may be harvested for drinking. Consume coconut in its raw form, as coconut oil, coconut milk, or coconut water. Rich in healthy fats that have been shown to help your brain function at its best, it also aids in weight loss and hormone regulation for both blood sugar and thyroid management.

SNACK FACTS

Coconuts are a rich source of potassium, and their water is a great alternative to conventional sports drinks, as it has no dye, sugar syrups, or excessive sodium. The husks and leaves can be used as material to make a variety of products for furnishing and decorating, and many societies give it cultural and religious significance.

CELINE CELERY.

Cool, crisp, and low-cal, celery is an important food source of conventional antioxidant nutrients such as vitamin C, beta-carotene, and manganese. But it's most noted for a wealth of antioxidant nutrients it derives from phytonutrients. ("Phyto" refers to the Greek word for plant.) This helps protect us against unwanted oxygen damage to our cells, blood vessels, and organ systems, and brings benefits to our digestive and cardiovascular systems.

SNACK FACTS

Celery comes in a variety of colors, from sheer white to lustrous gold to rich red and deep green. Super in a salad or sauce, and always up for a snack-time dip, celery is best consumed fresh.

CHARLIE CHERRY.

Get your hands on a bowl of cherries and thank us later. Burgundy Bings and the pink-flushed yellow Queen Annes are sweet, juicy, well-packed bundles of nutrition. And what's more fun than plucking a cherry from the stem with your teeth? Cool with desserts or perfect on their own, cherries might just be the perfect fruit. Research shows cherries — and especially tart cherry juice — can reduce arthritis pain and post-workout soreness, and even reduce your risk of heart disease and cancer. Plus they're cute.

SNACK FACTS

*F*avor fruits and vegetables that are deeply red, purple, and blue, as these are very high in anthocyanin, inflammation-reducing nutrients. The antioxidant potential ebbs soon after these foods are picked — so scoop them up and enjoy them right away.

CHUCKY CHICKEN.

Chicken, the most common type of poultry, is prepared as food in a wide variety of ways. We like ours broiled, fried, roasted, grilled, poached, and sautéed. (It's hard to choose a favorite.) No matter how you prepare yours, chicken is an excellent source of lean protein, which is required for optimal health at all ages. A mere four ounces of chicken meat fulfills roughly 68 percent of the daily-recommended value for protein, which reduces bone loss and prevents Alzheimer's disease in older people. Chicken also is a great source of niacin and selenium, both of which are directly related to reducing risk for certain cancers, and provides a rich source of vitamin B-6, which gives us energy and supports the cardiovascular system.

SNACK FACTS

*G*o for hormone-free chicken if you have that option. It's healthier. Also, and this is important, cook chicken meat thoroughly prior to consumption, as raw chicken meat commonly has the Salmonella organism, which can make you very sick if ingested. Wash all surfaces and hands that come in contact with raw chicken meat with soap and water. Don't take a chance. B'gawk!

COLBY CABBAGE.

Cabbage heads generally range from one to eight pounds and can be green, purple, or white. Smooth-leafed, firm-headed green cabbages are the most common. You can eat them raw or steam, pickle, stew, sauté, or braise them. Pickling is one of the most popular ways of preserving cabbage, creating dishes such as sauerkraut and kimchi. Cabbage provides the body with the most cardiovascular benefits when it is steamed: the fiber binds to bile acids to help remove cholesterol from the body. It also contains a special nutrient, sinigrin (also found in Brussels sprouts, broccoli, and the seeds of black mustard), which has been shown to help prevent bladder, colon, and prostate cancers.

SNACK FACTS

Aim to eat different colors of cabbage; the different colors contain different nutrients and antioxidants that are beneficial to the body in many ways. All colors are rich sources of fiber, vitamin C, and vitamin A. Cabbage also supports proper digestion by maintaining proper levels of bacteria, and maintains the linings of our intestinal and stomach walls to prevent and/or manage ulcers.

CONNOR CARROT.

The carrot is a root vegetable, usually orange in color, though purple, red, white, and yellow varieties exist. It has a crisp texture when fresh, and can be enjoyed raw, chopped, boiled, fried, steamed, cooked in soups and stews, given as baby and pet food, and — because they're so sweet — can be used in some fruit-like roles. (Think grated carrots in carrot cakes, puddings, and alone or with fruits in jam and preserves.) And carrot juice! Did we mention carrot juice? Delicious. Carrots are renowned for their rich supply of the antioxidant nutrient beta-carotene, and eating a quarter cup of carrots per day reduces your risk for developing cardiovascular disease. They also offer tremendous anti-inflammatory benefits, aid in vision health — specifically the prevention of glaucoma — and help prevent cancer.

SNACK FACTS

Although they supply vitamin A, which is important for restoring and maintaining vision, eating large quantities of carrots can't really help you see in the dark. That's a myth.

CONRAD COLLARD GREENS.

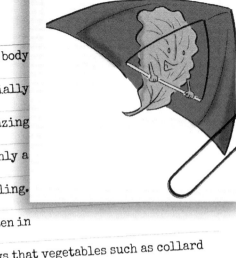

Collard greens, a cruciferous vegetable, have the ability to rid the body of certain toxins, reduce inflammation, and support digestion (especially if you have a tummy ache or reflux problems). They also have the amazing ability to lower cholesterol, especially when eaten steamed. Roughly a quarter pound of cooked collards contains 46 calories and is oh-so filling. High in vitamins C and K (the clotting vitamin), collards should be eaten in moderation by anyone taking blood thinners. Finally, research shows that vegetables such as collard greens have potent anti-viral, anti-bacterial, and anti-cancer agents, so they've earned our respect and a place at the table.

SNACK FACTS

Collard greens are a staple vegetable of Southern American cuisine. They're often prepared with similar green leaf vegetables — kale, turnip greens, spinach, and mustard greens — in mixed greens.

CORNELIUS CORN.

Corn, a tender annual that can grow four to twelve feet tall, is a member of the grass family. It produces one to three ears on a leafy stalk. The ears contain the grain, which are seeds called kernels, which in sweet corn can be yellow, white, black, red, or a combination of colors. In addition to being a barbecue staple — and everyone's favorite popped theater treat — corn is a unique phytonutrient-rich food that provides well-documented antioxidant benefits (and is a good source of vitamin C as well as the mineral manganese). Eat a variety of corn colors to get all of the health benefits.

SNACK FACTS

Call it corn or maize, it's been around for ages. Indigenous peoples in Mesoamerica domesticated it in prehistoric times.

COSMO CUCUMBER.

After tomatoes, cabbage, and onions, cucumbers are the fourth most widely cultivated vegetable in the world, and they're enjoyed in all types of cuisine. Related to melons (including watermelon and cantaloupe) and squashes (including summer squash, winter squash, zucchini, and pumpkin), cucumbers are usually more than 90 percent water. Overall it's a health bonanza. Look to cukes to reduce your risk of cardiovascular disease as well as several cancer types, including breast, uterine, ovarian, and prostate cancers. It's a valuable source of antioxidant nutrients such as vitamin C, beta-carotene, and manganese.

SNACK FACTS

The varieties of cucumbers are classified into three main varieties: "slicing," "pickling," and "burpless."

CURTIS CAULIFLOWER.

Cauliflower is part of the cruciferous vegetable family, which has health benefits above and beyond those of mere ordinary vegetables: detoxification, antioxidants (which protect our cells against cancer formation), anti-inflammation, heart health, and digestive support. They're also potent weapons against obesity and type 2 diabetes. Consume a cup or two of these two to three times per week to reap all the health benefits and more. Or crank it up a notch: enjoy cauliflower and other vegetables from the cruciferous vegetable group four to five times per week, and increase your serving size to two cups.

SNACK FACTS

Look at a cauliflower head (technically a "curd") up close. You'll see it's composed of undeveloped flower buds attached to a central stalk. When broken apart into separate buds, cauliflower looks like a little tree.

ENZO EGGPLANT.

Familiar to many as deep purple and glossy, eggplants are plum gorgeous. They belong to the nightshade family of vegetables, which includes tomatoes, sweet peppers, and potatoes. Their cream-colored flesh tastes pleasantly bitter, has a spongy texture, and in recipes balances the surrounding flavors of other, stronger-flavored, ingredients. What can they do for you? Everything from supporting your digestion with dietary fiber to building bones with manganese to keeping your enzymes catalyzing with molybdenum, to supplying your heart with needed potassium. And that's just the highlights.

SNACK FACTS

Eggplants dazzle as lavender, jade green, orange, and yellow-white, and come in sizes and shapes ranging from that of a small tomato to a large zucchini. They can be baked, roasted, or steamed.

EVIE EDAMAME.

Edamame (pronounced "eh-dah-MAH-may"), Japanese for "branched bean," are cheerful green soybeans. With their smooth texture and sweet flavor, edamame are fun to snack on and very easy to digest. The pods are boiled or steamed and served with salt. And have they got fiber! A half cup of these guys (shelled) offers 9 grams of fiber, about the same as in four slices of whole wheat bread or four cups of steamed zucchini. They also have nearly as much protein as they do carbohydrates. Rich in antioxidants and bursting with iron — that half-cup yields about as much iron as a 4-ounce roasted chicken breast — you've got a powerhouse vegetable you can eat like candy.

SNACK FACTS

Results from a new study in China suggest that eating more soybean protein may help prevent and treat hypertension. And pregnant women take note: the folic acid in edamame helps with fetal development.

GARY GARLIC.

Garlic is celebrated around the world for its pungent flavor as a seasoning and condiment. The garlic plant's bulb is the most commonly used part of the plant. With the exception of the single-clove types, garlic bulbs are normally divided into numerous fleshy sections called cloves. Garlic cloves are consumed raw or cooked, and have been used for medicinal purposes. Their pungent, spicy flavor mellows and sweetens considerably with cooking.

We're impressed with garlic because it may improve iron metabolism and it helps our blood vessels expand — keeping our blood pressure in check. Due to its high content of vitamin C, vitamin B-6, selenium, and manganese, it has also been shown to lower blood triglycerides and total cholesterol levels — so it protects against heart disease and type 2 diabetes.

SNACK FACTS

With a history of human use spanning 7,000 years, garlic is native to central Asia, and has long been a staple in the Mediterranean region, as well as a frequent seasoning in Asia, Africa, and Europe. Try it on pizza, it's spectacular!

GERTIE GREEN BEAN.

We know of more than 130 varieties of the humble green bean. Succulent and flavorful, they're favorites in the home garden. Pod color can be green, purple, red, or streaked. They can be thin or wide and are rich sources of carotenoids, which boost the immune system and help us see well. Moreover they're anti-inflammatory, which helps reduce our risk of type 2 diabetes — and they support bone and connective tissue development. Good to grow on!

SNACK FACTS

Also known as "string beans" or "snap beans," green beans are terrifically versatile. They're often steamed, boiled, stir-fried, or baked in casseroles. Wash them, snap off the ends, and they're ready to go.

GINA GINGER.

Ginger, or ginger root, isn't really a root at all, but rather a rhizome of the plant Zingiber officinale, and is consumed as a delicacy, medicine, or spice. (A rhizome is a stem that grows out from the plant underground, and from which small roots will sprout, as well as new green shoots.) It's related to turmeric, cardamom, and galangal, and is fibrous and gnarly looking — but plump with healthy juice and oils.

Generations of moms have known it as helpful in relieving kids' tummy aches, and scientists now know that it hinders the formation of inflammatory compounds. Better still, studies show that it's a safe and effective way to reduce nausea during pregnancy. One more? It reduces the risk for colorectal cancers.

SNACK FACTS

Grate or express ginger into just about any food or drink to get the health benefits. (Even ginger ale and candied ginger have healthful properties.) Ginger does have a strong smell and taste — if you find it unpleasant you can always buy it in supplement form. (Some folks are allergic to ginger; others should steer clear if a doctor says it might interfere with their medication.)

GORDON GRAPE.

Who doesn't love a bunch of grapes? Smooth-skinned, juicy, light green or deep red to purplish black, these berries can be eaten raw or pressed into work making wine, jam, juice, jelly, grape-seed extract, raisins, vinegar, and grape-seed oil. Their special plant nutrients are believed to play a role in longevity, are famous for promoting brain and heart health, and fight body-wide inflammation, tissue damage, and bad microbes. The total number of different antioxidant nutrients alone in grapes runs well into the hundreds.

SNACK FACTS

Chilled, baked, roasted, or grilled, grapes enhance all foods, from appetizers to salads and side dishes. Grapes sold commercially often leave the field with pesticides, so buy the organic varieties.

GREGORY GRAPEFRUIT.

Grapefruit, a large citrus fruit with a bitter yellow rind and inner skin and a highly flavored, somewhat acid, juicy pulp, is a great source of vitamins A and C, which help boost the immune system (specifically with inflammatory conditions such as asthma, osteoarthritis, and rheumatoid arthritis). As free radicals can oxidize cholesterol and lead to plaques that may rupture — causing heart attacks or stroke — vitamin C is on your side promoting cardiovascular health. It's part of a complete breakfast.

SNACK FACTS

The grapefruit was known as the shaddock or shattuck until the 19th century. Its current name alludes to clusters of the fruit on the tree, which often appear similar to grapes.

H2O.

Water is the most abundant compound on Earth's surface, covering about 70 percent of the planet. In nature, water exists in liquid, solid, and gaseous states, and it's true that we're mostly water by volume. A good thing, too: water is our body's main nutrient transport system. Without adequate water, the vitamins, minerals, and other nutrients we depend on essentially move through "sludge." In a state of dehydration we feel lethargic and unfocused. How much water should we drink? Aim to take in at least half your body weight in ounces of plain water per day. A 100-pound person would want 50 ounces, or 6.25 cups. That's doable, and you'll feel better for it.

SNACK FACTS

They're wet, sure, but juices, sodas, tea, coffee, and artificially sweetened sport beverages aren't plain water, and actually create a burden for your body, not health. If you don't like drinking plain water, sweeten it naturally with sliced lemons, limes, or berries. That's refreshing!

HILLARY HONEYDEW.

Honeydew, a pale, smooth-skinned winter melon with sweet, greenish flesh, is a rich source of potassium, adequate amounts of which can help manage and prevent high blood pressure. Honeydew is also a rich source of vitamin C, which boosts the immune system. Copper as a trace mineral is also found in honeydew, as are B vitamins, which get rid of toxins and can prevent Alzheimer's and heart disease.

SNACK FACTS

Honeydew's thick, juicy, sweet flesh is often eaten for dessert, though it makes a welcome treat anytime it's in season.

KENNY KALE.

Kale is a hardy cabbage with loose, curled, finely cut green or purple leaves. As a cruciferous vegetable it's related to broccoli, cauliflower, collard greens, and Brussels sprouts, and shares their boundless nutritional benefits — among them ridding the body of toxins, reducing inflammation, fighting the conditions that cause cancer, and keeping the cardiovascular system working at its best. What's more, Kale is low calorie, high fiber, fat free, and made for boosting your immune system.

SNACK FACTS

Anyone on a liver detox diet should load up on kale, which is filled with fiber and sulfur, both great for detoxifying the body and keeping the liver healthy. You've only got one liver, and it's working its heart out for you.

LOLITA LETTUCE.

Lettuce is an annual plant of the aster or sunflower family, and though it's most often grown as a leaf vegetable, we value its stem and seeds as well. Lettuce is most often tossed in salads, although it also finds work in soups, sandwiches, and wraps; it can also be grilled. The darker the lettuce, the better the nutrition, as dark, leafy greens are a swell source of vitamin K, which keeps calcium in the bones and out of the arteries. Also look to lettuce for carbohydrates, protein, a small amount of fat, other essential vitamins and minerals (largely found in the leaf), and dietary fiber (concentrated in the spine and ribs).

SNACK FACTS

There are several types of lettuce, but three (leaf, head, and cos or romaine) are the most common. Stem lettuce, widely consumed in China, is eaten either raw or cooked, the latter primarily in soups and stir-fry.

LUCY LEMON and LOGAN LIME.

Pucker up! Perhaps most interesting for their antibiotic effects, sour yellow lemons and green limes are terrific sources of vitamin C, which boosts the immune system and has been shown to protect against rheumatoid arthritis. Among the most alkaline, or acidic, fruits growing, and super-charged with anti-cancer nutrients called flavonoids, lemons have been shown to stop cell division in many cancer cell lines. They're perfect, all-natural dietary additions for anyone working to prevent cancer or support cancer remission and treatment.

SNACK FACTS

Lemons are used for culinary and non-culinary purposes throughout the world, primarily for its juice, though the pulp and rind (zest) are also used in cooking and baking. The juice of the lemon is about 5 percent to 6 percent citric acid, which gives it that sour taste. Limes are usually smaller and less sour than lemons.

44

LYDIA LIMA BEAN.

Whether you know them as lima beans or butter beans, these veggie treats are usually cream or green in color, and are delicately flavored. Their high fiber content prevents blood sugar levels from rising too rapidly after eating them, so they're great at helping balance blood sugar levels while providing steady, slow-burning energy. That's good news for all of us, but particularly those with diabetes and suffering with insulin resistance. The fiber also helps prevent heart disease, the bean's vegetable protein lowers cholesterol, and these beans' iron and manganese keep us feeling strong and ready for play.

SNACK FACTS

The lima bean plant (Phaseolus lunatus) is named after Lima, the capital city of Peru, where people have been eating them since 6,000 BC. In Spanish-speaking countries, such as Peru, Lima is pronounced "Lee-ma."

MALIK MUSHROOM.

Mushrooms are a low-calorie food eaten cooked or raw and as garnish to a meal. Dietary mushrooms are a good source of B vitamins, such as riboflavin, niacin, and pantothenic acid, as well as the essential minerals selenium, copper, and potassium. Their fat, carbohydrate, and calorie content are low. You won't find a lot of vitamin C or sodium here, but what mushrooms do for us is fantastic: evidence shows that mushrooms help lower our risk of arthritis, cancer, and cardiovascular disease by supporting balanced activities among the white blood cells of our immune system.

SNACK FACTS

Cooks tap mushrooms extensively all over the world — notably in China, Korea, Europe, Japan, and India — as mushrooms are esteemed as the "meat" of the vegetable world.

A SAFETY TIP

Don't eat mushrooms you find growing in the wild unless you know exactly what you're looking for (for example, you're a trained chef or wilderness expert). Unless you know what you're looking for, leave them be. (Many varieties aren't safe to eat, but many are.)

OCTAVIO ONION.

"To stay healthy, eat an onion a day." That's what Chris Kilham, "medicine hunter," who researches natural remedies all over the world, reported on the Fox News website recently. According to Kilham, the onion is a world-class superfood that "offers superior benefits for both the prevention and treatment of many common diseases, including various kinds of cancer, coronary heart disease, type 2 diabetes, cataracts and more. In addition, onions can act as a powerful antibiotic and are helpful in reducing food-borne illnesses caused by microbial contamination.

Raw onions are treasure chests of potent nutrients; even cooked they do a heck of a good job for us. Kilham concludes: "Chop onions into salads, cook them with vegetables, fish and meats, and find as many ways to eat them as possible."

SNACK FACTS

*W*hy does chopping onions make some people weep or cry? Such tearing up is a reflex we have to protect our eyes from irritants — in the case of onions, cutting them releases sulfur they've absorbed in the earth, which helps form a class of volatile organic molecules called amino acid sulfoxide. These molecules waft up, and we can't help but notice.

Interestingly, evidence shows that sulfur compounds in onion can lower blood levels of cholesterol and triglycerides, and improve cell membrane function in red blood cells. They've also been shown to help improve bone density, are anti-inflammatory, and have anti-cancer properties.

OLIVIA OLIVE.

Olives are an ancient food, thought to have originated in Crete, a Greek island. The fruit of the olive tree, olives are mostly fat, sodium, and carbohydrates (but not much of the latter). And this is good fat we're talking about. Three-quarters of the fat in olives is oleic acid, a monounsaturated fat that lowers blood cholesterol levels, promotes the development of bones and marrow, helps maintain metabolic balance, and fights oxidization, which is a chemical process that causes certain ailments.

Both olives and their oil are also a good source of vitamin E and other beneficial phytonutrient compounds, which appear to have significant anti-inflammatory properties, delay aging, and assist in the restoration of body tissues, both internal and external. More proof of olives' excellence? They also offer protection against cancer, atherosclerosis, liver disorders and inflammations, and infections.

SNACK FACTS

The olive is a small "drupe," a fleshy fruit with thin skin and a central stone containing the seed, just as plums, cherries, and almonds have. Olives are harvested in the green to purple stage; canned black olives may contain chemicals (usually ferrous sulfate) that turn them black artificially. What Americans call an olive pit or rock, the British call a stone.

SNACK FACTS

Diana Rattray, a Southern cooking expert, notes okra can be served raw, marinated in salads, or cooked on its own, and goes well with tomatoes, onions, corn, peppers, and eggplant. Whole, fresh okra pods also make excellent pickles. Its mild flavor can be compared to eggplant, though the texture, she says, is unusual. Well, okra is okra.

OMAR OKRA.

Okra, known in many English-speaking countries as lady's fingers, bhindi, or gumbo, is a flowering plant in the mallow family, and valued for its edible green seedpods. Dig in: it's a powerhouse of valuable nutrients, nearly half of which is soluble fiber in the form of gums and pectins. (Soluble fiber helps to lower serum cholesterol, reducing the risk of heart disease.) The other half is insoluble fiber, which helps to keep the intestinal tract healthy — and that decreases the risk of some forms of cancer, especially colorectal cancer.

Rich in vitamins A, C, K, and folate, and the minerals iron, calcium, manganese, and magnesium, okra promotes a healthy immune system while developing happy, healthy organs and bones.

ORLANDO ORANGE.

As attractive as they are tasty, sweet oranges speak to warm, sunny days, light breezes, and starry nights. Rich in ascorbic acid, or vitamin C, oranges are important for the body's manufacture of collagen, the protein responsible for connecting cells, muscles, and bones. Vitamin C and other phytonutrients in oranges boost the immune system.

It's best to eat the orange rather than just drink the juice, as with the whole fruit you're getting antioxidants and nutrients found in the peel and inner white pulp of the fruit. Processing the fruit into juice strips out many of the nutrients.

SNACK FACTS

The sweet orange is known as "Chinese apple" in several modern languages. As for how it's built, the orange generally has ten segments (called carpels) inside, contains up to six seeds (or pips), and has a porous white tissue — called pith or, more properly, mesocarp or albedo — lining its rind. Orange you glad you asked?

PASQUALE PEPPERS.

Let's get spicy. There are five main species of peppers, covering the sweetly meaty treats bell, sweet, and many standard chili peppers, such as ancho, jalapeño, and cayenne; datil, habanero, and Scotch bonnet; Tabasco and Thai; South American rocoto; and the ají peppers. These are all excellent sources of more than 30 members of the carotenoid nutrient family, known for protecting the cardiovascular system and blood sugar regulation. Peppers also are a rich source of vitamins A and C, which boost the immune system.

SNACK FACTS

The reason some peppers are hot — ay yi yi! — is that some plants would rather people and other mammals not eat them. They would rather birds eat them, as birds tend to eat and scatter the seeds of the fruit, which produces more pepper plants. So hot peppers contain capsaicin, a chemical that mammals — not birds — detect as "hot." Some people find this eye-watering mouthful a delicious challenge, of course, proving that we're smarter than the average pepper plant.

PAULIE PEAR.

Juicy, soft, and often sweet, pears belong to the rose family of plants, Rosaceae, which includes apples, apricots, cherries, chokeberry, crabapples, loquats, peaches, plums, quinces, raspberries, serviceberries, and strawberries, as well as the almond, which is a tree nut. Pears typically have a rounded body that tapers into a neck.

Pears are rich in conventional antioxidants such as vitamin E and omega-3 fatty acids, and offer an array of flavonols and carotenoids. Science shows that pears help reduce your risk of chronic inflammation (arthritis), excessive oxidative stress, heart disease, type 2 diabetes, and even cancer.

Enjoy pears raw, either whole or sliced into salads. For variety, check this out: Anjou pears are firm and mild-flavored; Bartletts bring the juice; Bosc pears are crisp and sweet; Asian pears are all about crunch and are very mild; Comice pear flesh is less grainy than that of classic pears, and has a sparkly flavor; French butter pears are happy to please, but do make sure they're completely ripe before you chow down.

SNACK FACTS

Pear skin contains at least three to four times as many plant-based nutrients as the flesh itself — and has been shown to contain about half of the fruit's total dietary fiber. And that's the skinny on pears.

PENELOPE PINEAPPLE.

Consumed fresh, cooked, juiced, or preserved, pineapple abounds in a wide array of cuisines. A tropical plant with edible multiple fruit consisting of coalesced berries, it is indigenous to South America. Chunks of pineapple not only are used in desserts, such as fruit salad, but also are a main ingredient in savory dishes, such as on hamburgers and as a pizza topping. Crushed pineapple is used in yogurt, jam, sweets, and ice cream. The juice of the pineapple is delicious as a beverage.

Notably, pineapples contain manganese and bromelain, a complex mixture of substances that can be extracted from the stem and core fruit of the pineapple. Bromelain is known to help proper digestion and afford possible cancer protection. The high vitamin A, C, and E content of pineapples also helps boost the immune system and vision health.

SNACK FACTS

A pineapple will never become any riper than it was when harvested. For that reason, a fully ripe pineapple can bruise and rot quickly. If you store yours at room temperature, use it within two days; if you refrigerate it, you've got perhaps seven days, which ought to be enough time to do something fun with it.

BONUS FACT

Certain bat-pollinated wild pineapples open their flowers only at night. Bats!

PERCY PEACH.

Peaches and nectarines are the same species, even though they're regarded commercially as different fruits. Nectarines have an orange center and faint fuzz, while peaches boast white centers and fuzzy skin.

What's in it for you? Peaches are a rich source of both vitamins and minerals including vitamins A, C, E, and K, along with thiamin, riboflavin, vitamin B-6, niacin, folate, and potassium, all of which contribute to healthy vision, blood pressure, and bones. Peaches' rich antioxidants and high fiber also promote healthy digestion and colon health, and help ward off cancer and cardiovascular disease.

SNACK FACTS

The scientific name persica, from "Prunus persica," along with the word "peach" itself and its relatives in many European languages, comes from an early European belief that peaches were native to Persia. The ancient Romans referred to the peach as malum persicum, "Persian apple," later becoming French pêche, hence the English "peach." But peaches are actually native to northwest China. Booya! Now you know.

PETER PUMPKIN.

Pumpkin, a gourd-like squash, is native to North America and typically has a thick orange or yellow shell, creased from the stem to the bottom, containing the seeds and pulp. It's one of the most popular crops in the United States, with 1.5 billion pounds produced each year — no doubt because in America and Canada they're Halloween and Thanksgiving staples making their way into soups, purées, and pies, and are carved out and grinning as jack-o'-lanterns.

Most parts of the pumpkin are edible, including the fleshy shell, the seeds, the leaves, and even the flowers. And a good thing, too, as one serving of pumpkin contains twice the recommended daily value for vitamin A, along with a powerful antioxidant called beta-carotene — both of which, when eaten, help with vision health and reduce one's risk for cancer.

Pumpkin is also rich in fiber, which helps you feel fuller longer, leading to fewer cravings for junk food. All the while pumpkin protects your heart from cardiovascular disease. The seeds — roast them for a treat — are rich in phytonutrients that have been shown to reduce harmful LDL cholesterol levels.

SNACK FACTS

Pumpkins are no strangers to plumping up. The current world record holder is Tim Mathison's 2,032-pound pumkin, grown in Napa, California, which trounced Ron Wallace's 2012 record of 2.009 pounds. No trick; all treat.

PIERRE POTATO.

Appearing in a variety of colors, shapes, and sizes, the potato is starchy — it's best known for its carbohydrate content — and packed with power. A great source of potassium, vitamin B-6, and vitamin C, the potato helps boost your immune system and keeps you from getting sick. It's a gluten-free starch, good to know if you need to strike gluten from your diet for health or fitness reasons.

Potatoes also contain carotenoids, flavonoids, and caffeic acid, health-promoting compounds that exhibit activity against free radicals and support optimal blood pressure, cardiovascular function, and athletic performance.

Potatoes are prepared skin-on or peeled, whole or cut up, and with seasonings or without. The only requirement involves cooking to swell the starch granules. Most potato dishes are served hot, but some are first cooked, and then served cold, notably potato salad and potato chips. Moreover, potato starch is used in the food industry to thicken and bind soups and sauces.

SNACK FACTS

Store your spuds in a dark, well-ventilated area. If yours develop green areas or start to sprout, trim those bits off before using. Also, let's give our thanks to Hasbro for the Mr. Potato Head toy. We're glad they didn't come out with Mr. Kale Head instead. As much as we love kale, this is better.

PETEY PORK.

Pork is the culinary name for meat from the domestic pig. Uncured and non-processed cuts of pork are marketed as "the other white meat," with these leaner cuts ringing out as a rich source of protein and essential amino acids that the body requires to thrive. Pork is nutritionally similar to poultry, the original white meat.

Many people enjoy pork freshly cooked and preserved. Curing extends its shelf life, so that's where you'll find hams, smoked pork, gammon, bacon, and sausage.

SNACK FACTS

Fresh pork may contain trichinosis, a kind of infection, so the USDA recommends cooking ground pork to an internal temperature of 160°F, followed by a three-minute rest, and cooking whole cuts to a minimum internal temperature of 145°F, also followed by a three-minute rest. Jewish and Islamic dietary laws forbid the consumption of pork. That said, it's one of the most widely eaten meats in the world, accounting for about 38 percent of meat production worldwide, although consumption varies widely from place to place. It can be eaten nose to tail: yum!

PRUDENCE PEA.

A pea is a most commonly green, occasionally purple or golden yellow, pod-shaped vegetable, widely vine-grown as a cool-season crop. (Botanically speaking, peapods are a fruit, as they contain seeds developed from the ovary of a (pea) flower. However, in cooking, we consider peas to be vegetables.)

Peas are usually boiled or steamed, which breaks down the cell walls and makes them taste sweeter and their nutrients more "bioavailable," or ready to go to work for you. Starchy but high in fiber, protein, vitamins, minerals, and lutein, peas are about one-quarter protein and one-quarter sugar when measured by dry weight. That explains why they taste sweet and are packed with pep. They have a special compound that's been shown to protect specifically against stomach cancer. Green peas are a reliable source of anti-inflammatory omega-3 fats in the form of antioxidant-rich alpha-linolenic acid.

SNACK FACTS

In the mid-19th century, Austrian monk Gregor Mendel's observations of pea pods led to the principles of Mendelian genetics, the foundation of modern genetics. He ended up growing and examining about 28,000 pea plants in the course of his experiments.

REX RASPBERRY.

Red, black, and purple, raspberries are a key commercial fruit crop, widely grown in all temperate regions of the world. They are traditionally a midsummer crop, but with new technology, cultivars, and transportation, they can now be had year-round.

An individual raspberry weighs a tiny fraction of an ounce and is made up of around a hundred drupelets, each of which consists of a juicy pulp and a single central seed. A raspberry bush can yield several hundred berries a year.

They may be small, but nutritionally they pack a punch: they offer among the highest known value of dietary fiber in whole foods, weighing in at up to 20 percent fiber per total weight, or 32 percent daily value per cup. They're also rich in vitamin C, with a cup yielding about 54 percent daily value, and manganese, about 41 percent daily value. As well, you're looking at raspberries bringing to the table B vitamins 1–3, folic acid, magnesium, copper, and iron.

SNACK FACTS

Raspberries also have ketones, compounds that give them their fruity smell and help fight obesity and fatty liver disease. Plus, did we mention they're raspberries? Enjoy!

SAMANTHA SEAFOOD.

Seafood is any form of sea life that humans regard as food, and prominently includes fish and shellfish. Shellfish include various species of mollusks, crustaceans, and spiny-skinned echinoderms.

Edible sea plants, such as some seaweeds and microalgae, are widely eaten as seafood around the world, especially in Asia. In North America we extend seafood to include freshwater organisms eaten by humans, so all edible aquatic life may be referred to as seafood.

As always, quality counts, but particularly here. Local, wild-caught and inspected seafood is your best choice for freshness, health, and flavor. Cold-water fish such as salmon contain a rich amount of omega-3 fatty acids, which help protect against and manage inflammatory diseases including heart disease, high blood pressure, and type 2 diabetes.

Shellfish and saltwater fish are lean sources of protein; they also are good sources of iodine, which in some people can boost thyroid and adrenal function. Cholesterol conscious? The naturally occurring cholesterol in shellfish (and eggs) is not as harmful to the heart as we once believed, so it's not necessary to cut shellfish out of your diet if you have high cholesterol. Just enjoy it in moderation instead.

SNACK FACTS

Speaking of cholesterol, hydrogenated oil, or trans fats, the most harmful to the heart, are found in processed snacks, pastries, and condiments. These you should avoid completely. And we're not squidding around with this one.

SAMMY SLEEP.

Good morning.

Everybody sleeps. Mammals, other birds, reptiles, amphibians, and even fish get shut-eye, so you're in good company when your head hits the pillow. We sleep in part to allow our bodies to repair damage, grow new cells and tissues, fight off ailments, detoxify, and allow hormones to regulate.

Without enough sleep we're prone to weight gain, adrenal failure, thyroid dysfunction, poor insulin regulation, and — eventually — death. Sleep difficulties are closely associated with psychiatric disorders such as depression, alcoholism, and bipolar disorder.

So how much sleep is enough? Adults should sleep 7 to 8 hours per night. Children need 10 to 12 hours of sleep per night for optimal growth.

Here's something: studies show exercise generally improves sleep for most people, and helps sleep disorders such as insomnia. The optimum time to exercise may be four to eight hours before bedtime, though exercise at any time of day is beneficial, with the exception of heavy exercise taken shortly before bedtime, which may disturb sleep.

Also, try not to eat past, say, 7 o'clock at night. If you go to sleep with a full belly, your body will be up all night trying to digest your meal, and will have little energy left for sleep's other benefits. (For this reason, too, avoid late-night snacks. Though you can certainly dream of them.)

SOLOMON SPINACH.

From savoy spinach's crisp, creased, curly leaves, to smooth-leafed spinach's flat, spade shapes, to baby spinach's salad-friendly taste and delicate texture, spinach is a true gift from nature. Look for the leaves with robust, healthy color, as these offer much greater concentrations of vitamin C — and are far and away more nourishing — than pale spinach leaves. Indeed, it's the vitamin C that protects all the oxygen-sensitive phytonutrients in the spinach that makes its leaves so vivacious on your plate and, when you eat them, in your body's cells.

Spinach and related foods, such as beets, chard, and quinoa, have unique properties in their pigmentation and other compounds that support our nervous system health — including specialized nervous system organs such as the eye.

Why stop there? Spinach protects our bodies from ailments related to inflammation and oxidative stress in the cardiovascular and skeletal systems, including cancers. In addition to vitamins C and K, spinach contains an array of nutrients such as vitamin E, beta-carotene, and manganese, and is an excellent source of the antioxidants selenium and zinc.

SNACK FACTS

Spinach is a power plant, but it won't give you Popeye-scale biceps. It does, however, ring in with the next best thing: the vitamin K provided by spinach yields twice the daily recommended value in one cup of fresh spinach leaves, and more than 1,000 percent of the daily value in one cup of boiled spinach, which contains about six times as much spinach — and that's important for maintaining bone health. Grow big and strong. Grow green.

STUART STRAWBERRY.

The strawberry is not a true botanical berry; it's what botanists call an "aggregate accessory fruit" akin to figs, mulberries, apples, and pears. With accessory fruits, the fleshy part is derived not from the plant's ovaries, but rather from the receptacle that holds the ovaries. Each apparent "seed," or achene, on the outside of the fruit is actually one of the ovaries of the flower, with a seed inside it.

However strawberries are classified, they're certainly snapped up for their aroma, bright red color, juicy texture, and sweetness. We eat them fresh or in prepared foods such as preserves, juices, pies, ice creams, and milkshakes. They're also great when dipped in chocolate, always in moderation.

In addition to being delicious, this fruit is very low in saturated fat, cholesterol, and sodium; and a good source of folate and potassium; and a solid source of dietary fiber and manganese. And the strawberry is among the top 20 fruits in antioxidant capacity, with one serving of about eight strawberries providing more vitamin C than an orange.

These amazing morsels help keep blood sugars within normal limits and hold inflammation away, which helps prevent high blood pressure and heart disease.

Try to eat fresh strawberries within a day or two, as this fragile fruit soon loses its vitamin C. Freeze them or buy them frozen, and they'll last much longer — and you can even blend them into smoothies that way for a yummy drink.

SNACK FACTS

People allergic to red strawberries might have much better luck with the yellow or white varieties, and there's a virtually allergen-free strawberry cultivar on the market called Sofar.

TABITHA TURKEY.

According to Smithsonian.com, which knows all about such matters, there are six subspecies of wild turkey, all native to North America. "The pilgrims hunted and ate the eastern wild turkey, M. gallopavo silvestris, which today has a range that covers the eastern half of the United States and extends into Canada. These birds, sometimes called the forest turkey, are the most numerous of all the turkey subspecies, numbering more than five million," the site says.

Turkeys can run at speeds of up to 25 miles per hour and fly as fast as 55 miles per hour, the site tells us. They're also delicious, as generations of Thanksgiving diners have proven. (Sorry, birds.)

Nutritionally, turkey is a great source of lean protein that can be eaten all year round. Turkey was recently shown to help keep post-meal insulin levels in desirable range, and it's high in B vitamins, phosphorus, selenium, zinc, and choline, all of which keep the immune system strong and prevent the body from breaking down essential amino acids.

SNACK FACTS

Again, from Smithsonian.com: "Benjamin Franklin never proposed the turkey as a symbol for America, but he did once praise it as being 'a much more respectable bird' than the bald eagle."

TOM TOMATO.

Originally from Mexico, and spread around the world following the Spanish colonization of the Americas, the tomato is consumed raw and as an ingredient in many dishes, sauces, salads, and drinks. Although botanically speaking it's a fruit, we consider it a vegetable for culinary purposes. (The United States Supreme Court has said so.)

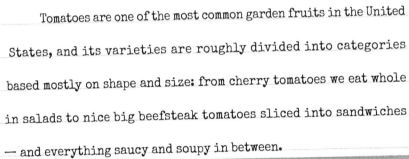

Tomatoes are one of the most common garden fruits in the United States, and its varieties are roughly divided into categories based mostly on shape and size: from cherry tomatoes we eat whole in salads to nice big beefsteak tomatoes sliced into sandwiches — and everything saucy and soupy in between.

Tomatoes offer ample vitamin C and E, manganese, and beta-carotene. Also within the fruit is a wealth of dietary lycopene, which lowers total cholesterol levels, triglyceride levels and LDL cholesterol in the blood stream. That protects the cardiovascular system — specifically the arteries — from clogging. Enjoy a tomato today.

WEREWOLF FACTS

Tomatoes belong to the genus lycopersicum, which means "wolf peach," a direct translation from another term for the fruit, the German Wolfpfirsich. Here's the story: German werewolf myths held that the tomato resembled the deadly nightshade, and that witches and sorcerers consume tomatoes in potions to transform themselves into werewolves. To date there have been no scientific studies on the effects of tomato consumption on witches and sorcerers.

SNACK FACTS

Keep tomatoes unwashed, at room temperature, and out of direct sunlight. Don't refrigerate them, as this can degrade the flavor. Keep unripened tomatoes in a paper bag until they're ready. (Storing the stem down will prolong shelf life.)

TIBERIUS TURNIP GREENS.

The leaves of the turnip root, turnip greens are bitter due to their wonderful calcium content, and easily outscore cruciferous cousins cabbage, kale, cauliflower, and broccoli in glucosinolate content, which offer cancer-preventing properties. Eat these guys regularly as you should from a variety of cruciferous veggies. We recommend including cruciferous vegetables — starring turnip greens — in your diet four to five times a week, and in servings of 1.5 to two cups.

Steaming turnip greens is best for your health. Cut them into half-inch slices, and let them sit for at least five minutes to draw out their health-promoting properties, and steam for 5 minutes. Toss with a good dressing and enjoy.

The benefit to you: you'll detoxify faster, fight inflammation, enjoy greater heart health, and digest your meals better, which will give all your organs and tissues a needed boost.

SNACK FACTS

Soak and rinse your greens four or five times to get all the grit out, then go to town on the seasoning. Add salt pork to the pot? Ham hocks? Cook the leaves with chicken broth, bacon, garlic, onions, or wine? Drawing on Southern respect for cooks and their greens, where passions run high, we'll leave it up to you.

WALLY WATERMELON.

Watermelon fruit, coming from a vine-like flowering plant originally from southern Africa, is only loosely considered a type of melon: it's what botanists call a pepo, a berry that has a thick rind and fleshy center. And that center is juicy and sweet, usually deep red to pink, but sometimes orange, yellow, or white.

Nutritionally, watermelon, like tomatoes, are a rich source of lycopene, key in controlling harmful lipids in the bloodstream that otherwise might clog up the arteries. Other compounds can help improve blood flow, promote muscle recovery, spur healing, and deliver other aspects of our cardiovascular health. Watermelon contains about 6 percent sugar and 91 percent water by weight. As with fruits generally, it is an abundant source of vitamin C.

SNACK FACTS

Not to overwhelm your picnic, but there are more than 1,200 varieties of watermelon ranging in weight from less than one pound to more than 200 pounds. You can get them with seeds and without.

Power Up *with* Green Box Comics

What would you do if you had tremendous speed, amazing strength, and the power of a universe of friends and allies? Congratulations, you do! Join Knute Trition, Ed Yucation, X. R. Cise, and their team on the League of Nutritious Justice as they battle the Legion of Unhealthy Injustice, led by the diabolical villain O.BC.D. Twenty-six out-of-this-world comic book stories are here, yours for the taking, and each one shows where the real power lies: in you, in the power of choice. Use your superpowers for good health and there'll be no stopping you.

63

Adam Apple was out for his morning run, and was on his last trip around the block, when a shadow caught his eye. Suddenly Knute Trition was there, flying in front of him — backwards and upside down. They were facing each other.

"Hi, Adam," said Knute.

"Good morning, Knute," said Adam, who kept running. He wanted to point out that Knute was upside down, but decided Knute was probably already aware of it.

"I don't mean to interrupt your run, but I was on my way to a big battle against O.BC.D., and needed your advice," Knute said.

"Sure thing," said Adam. He was always happy to help.

Knute flew a quick circle around Adam just for fun, then pretended to do the backstroke alongside him as they continued down the street.

"I've noticed that you run all the time and never really get winded. You get tired eventually, but I never see you gasping for air. What's your secret?"

Adam was flattered that Knute had noticed that he was in good shape. In truth, he did love a good run, particularly the nice warm feeling it gave him, and seeing all the trees, houses, and people he encountered on his outing. This was the first time anyone had noticed that he had great lung power.

"It's simple, Knute. There's scientific proof that the more apples you eat in a week, the better your lungs work. You can take in more air and keep your cells fed with oxygen for all the important work you have to do."

"Cool!" said Knute, who then turned himself upright, touched down, and ran alongside Adam. "I had no idea."

Adam continued: "Apples are full of antioxidant-like phytonutrients that reduce the risk of cancer and heart attacks. Apples are incredibly healthful, and delicious." Adam knew all about apples.

They jogged on for a few moments together.

"Is this something you can use against O.BC.D.?" Adam finally asked.

"I think so," said Knute. "Apple power sounds like one of the things that can defeat O.BC.D. I'm going to head on up to the orchard, get a basket of apples, and hand them out around town. That'll shut that bad guy down for a while."

Adam was about to say goodbye to his friend when Knute shot a mile into the sky, heading in the direction of Apex Orchards. He was fast.

"'Bye, Knute, good luck!" Adam called anyway.

On his way home he thought how nice it would be to fly. But then, feeling how strong his legs were, and enjoying the cool air and pleasant views at ground level, he decided he was happier to keep running.

THE GREEN BOX LEAGUE OF

NUTRITIOUS JUSTICE

Spell Me

Adam _ _ _ _ _ _ _

Allie Asparagus was steamed. Knute was supposed to meet her at the park at ten o'clock to go roller-skating. She checked the time on her phone: it was now ten twenty-five, and Knute hadn't shown up or even called. Other kids in the park were zipping around on in-line skates, roller skates like hers, and skateboards.

While she waited she practiced her moves: skating backwards, moonwalking, and her newest trick, the four-wheeler, where she rolled on only two wheels with each skate. Tall and lithe, she moved with purpose and power.

"You're getting really good at that," came a bright, happy voice behind her. It was X. R. Cise — Xandra Risa Cise — one of the founding members of the Green Box League of Nutritious Justice, who rolled up next to her on a pair of sleek in-line skates. Allie was surprised to see her, and the two friends hugged while twirling once in a quick circle.

"Thanks, Xandra! I'm sticking with it. I fell down a few times when I was starting to practice the four-wheeler, but now my balance and coordination are much better and I've got this down pat. I wonder what else I can do!"

Xandra smiled. "Have you tried ice skating? That's such a graceful way to move. If you haven't, I know you'll love it."

Just as Allie was about to say that her brothers were showing her how to ice-skate so she could play hockey with them, a giant pink cupcake shambled past as fast as it could go, trailing fast-food wrappers, half-eaten candy bars, and globs of fuchsia frosting.

Everybody watched as a few moments later Knute Trition sailed through the crowd on skates. "Excuse me, pardon me, nice to see you, hello, hey, lookin' good," he said as he weaved through the crowd, comfortably in pursuit.

"Allie! Hi! Sorry I'm late," he said, and then he was gone. He dipped down to pick up litter as he went, but he was clearly after that cupcake, which was getting in everybody's way.

"It's O.BC.D.," Xandra said. "That creep never quits."

Allie watched as, every so often when it appeared Knute was going to catch him, the wily villain turned on a dime. He was exhausted, but determined not to get caught. Knute was smiling. This was fun for him.

Now Allie was *really* steamed. "This is supposed to be my date. I'm not going to let that lumbering mass of fast food slow me down," she said.

Xandra was about to offer to help, when Allie, having straightened her helmet and kneepads, took off like a shot, skating even faster than Knute.

"Allie, I've almost got this wrapped up," Knute called after, but this asparagus spear was having none of it. Blazing past Knute, she caught up to Obie, who looked at her in surprise. She hip-checked him hard, and the doughy mass went sailing overhead and landed in a cotton candy stall, whose proprietor had ducked out of the way at the last moment.

Allie braked to a stop, smoothing her outfit. Knute caught up to her.

"Wow," he said. "You did this?"

"Are you free to skate with me now?" Allie

asked sweetly.

"Uh ... What about Obie?"

"Oh, someone will be along to collect him. He's not my problem anymore," she said.

Taking Knute by the arm, she led him toward the heart of the park. She wanted to show him some tricks. On the way they passed Xandra, who was going to see about the still-dazed villain, now covered in puffs of cotton candy.

Xandra was smiling. "Hang on to that one, Knute; she's got fiber."

"Fiber and a sunny disposition," Allie amended.

Knute had to agree. And she could moonwalk, too.

70

THE GREEN BOX LEAGUE OF
NUTRITIOUS JUSTICE
Spell Me
Allie
COLOR US!

Sweet, smart, and ready to rumble, Angel Avocado is a full-on master of tae kwon do. Well, she's an orange belt, but she's a natural, as anyone who's seen her jumping reverse hook kick will tell you.

She's also slightly too young to be a full-fledged member of the Green Box League of Nutritious Justice, as Ed Yucation, visiting her in front of her home after school, has just told her — and immediately regretted being the bearer of bad news.

"Whaddaya mean I'm too young? Did you see the way I rock-'em sock-'emed Salty Snake? Gave the old hiii-ya to Di A. Betes? Remember that time O.BC.D. was going through everyone's lunch boxes and sticking in all that high-fructose corn syrup? I gave him the old heave-ho, and he's got the black eye to prove it!"

Ed was now backed up against Angel's picket fence. He tried to get a word in edgewise, but she plowed ahead.

"I'm not too young to babysit! I'm not too young to tutor language arts! I'm not too young to win the Presidential Active Lifestyle Award!"

"I know, I know ..." Ed began.

Now she was poking him in the chest as she spoke.

"Is it because I'm green skinned and fleshy? I'll have you know I'm beautiful! [Poke] I'm beautiful and brainy and perfect! [Poke] I'm Angel Avocado [Poke], and I pack a punch!"

"Angel, please," Ed tried one last time. "Let me finish."

Angel crossed her arms. "Let's have it, mister. Do I get to be a superhero?"

Ed considered his options. She was fast and furious, this one. And she needed a little help practicing self-control. But, well ... Should she get to join the League four months early? The fire in her eyes said yes. Knute would say yes, too, and work with her to help her control her passions.

"What the heck, Angel. You'll have time to ripen. Welcome to the League."

Angel Avocado was so excited she squealed, did a backflip, and then ran up to hug Ed Yucation, who smiled in relief.

That could have gone worse, he figured: she might have been a black belt.

THE GREEN BOX LEAGUE OF

NUTRITIOUS JUSTICE

Spell Me

Angel _ _ _ _ _ _ _ _ _ _

They don't come much tougher than Artie Artichoke, whose many broad florets and pointy tips would seem to say, "Keep away." But that impression hides the truth, which is that, underneath, Artie has a heart of gold.

He's squat and short, and puts his power to good use when fighting alongside Knute Trition and all his other friends in the Green Box League of Nutritious Justice.

Today he and Knute were just leaving the gym after a workout when they heard a little trumpet play: it was Knute's smartphone. They stopped outside by their bikes while Knute read a text message his mom had just sent:

"Hi, honey. Please pick up milk, eggs, and toothpaste on your way home. Don't forget to wrap your present for your dad's birthday party, and do be careful fighting crime. We love you so. Hugs and kisses, Mom."

"Aww," teased Artie, who'd sneaked a peek at the text when Knute read it. "Hugs and kisses from mom. Ain't that sweet."

"Yeah, yeah. Well, no fair eavesdropping," Knute said, typing out a brief reply. And then he smiled. "I've got an idea: let's race to the store! Whoever gets there first wins." Artie agreed.

When both boys were on their bikes, Knute counted down: three, two, one. Go!" And he took off like a shot.

Artie pedaled after him, but his legs were shorter, and the trip took longer. When he caught up to Knute at the store, he was surprised to find his friend being surrounded by a ring of goons: O.BC.D.'s boys. They were in poor shape, but there were a lot of them, and they had Knute with his back against the brick wall.

"All right, Knute Trition, we finally got you. The boss is gonna be happy when he hears we got you to eat a whole chocolate cake, frosting and all!" And indeed one of the goons was advancing toward Knute with a delicious-looking double-decker cake. Knute had nowhere to run. He seemed done for.

"Actually, fellas, I like a little cake once in a while. But I know when to say when, see," he said confidently. "And as it happens, I'm not hungry just now."

With that he launched himself away from the wall, toward the big fellow holding the cake, and flipped it over into his face. The goon staggered back, blubbering. Artie saw that as his cue, and started ramming the other guys in the seat of the pants with his sharp leaf tips, and they, too, howled.

Finally, they scattered.

After a few moments, Knute licked his fingers. There was a little chocolate frosting on them. "Not bad. I might have liked a small piece. A shame it's somebody's hat now."

Then they entered the store.

Artie turned around and smiled: "That's not all that's too bad, Knute: I'm in the store first. Looks like I won the race."

Knute laughed. It was true. Artie had won fair and square. But that was OK. This was one defeat that tasted sweeter to him than any victory.

THE GREEN BOX LEAGUE OF

NUTRITIOUS JUSTICE

Spell Me

Artie __ __ __ __ __ __ __ __ __ __ __

"Ladies and gentlemen, boys and girls, Beauregard Banana!"

And with that introduction, Beauregard leaped out of the wings, seemed to glide onto the stage, and with a peppy piano and drums behind him, launched right into his famous dance routine, his white spats flying on the polished wood of the stage with an exciting clickety-clack.

A thunderous applause followed and quickly subsided as the crowd settled back to enjoy the set.

When Beauregard danced and sang to "Puttin' on the Ritz," his whole long, yellow body seemed to float, supported by the ebbs and flows of the music. Smooth as hot fudge, fresh as bread, Beauregard filled the minutes with rhythm, light, and life, and the audience forgot all their cares.

Beauregard had that effect on people, and lived to slip and slide in the most appealing way. There was an energy and vitality about him that everyone recognized as bright and wonderful.

Beauregard practiced all the time, and had a twice-daily routine for stretching, which was great for building strength, flexibility, and balance.

Now, as the horns kicked in, he knew he would need all his strength to keep the crowd entertained and lower the boom on two oily villains in the Cholesterol Gang from the Legion of Unhealthy Injustice, whom he had just seen sneak past the stage manager to attempt to sabotage the show.

Resembling tubs of bacon and butter, these goons were trying for lights-out.

Without missing a beat, Beauregard did a backflip, five cartwheels to stage right, wrapped his cane around one thug, and smashed his hat down upon the head and shoulders of the other, trapping them both.

"How'd he do it?" one asked the other.

"I never even saw him coming!" the other said to the one.

Five cartwheels to stage left, Beauregard wound up back in the spotlight to take his bow — and nobody knew how close they'd come to disaster.

The next day the newspaper headlines read, "The Show Must Go On for Hero Banana," and "Cholesterol Meets a 'Bunch' of Trouble."

A proud Beauregard added the stories to his bulging scrapbook of exploits starring the League of Nutritious Justice.

And then? Why, he began practice for his next performance.

THE GREEN BOX LEAGUE OF
NUTRITIOUS JUSTICE

Spell Me
Beauregard

__ __ __ __ __ __ __ __

colorus

t's not easy starring in a music video one day, teaching choir the next, and fighting crime the day after, but Bianca Broccoli loves the work — that's why she can pack it all into the same day and make it look effortless.

LEAFY SCENE: Bianca, might we have a few moments of your time for *Leafy Scene* magazine? Our readers would love to read an interview with you.

BIANCA: Of course, darling. Ask your questions.

LEAFY SCENE: First, when did you start singing?

BIANCA: I have always sung, darling. I sing. It's what I do. La la la!

LEAFY SCENE: And what was it like starring in your latest video?

BIANCA: Fabulous, darling, fabulous. The song is one of my favorites: "*Vitamin D, My Dear,*" which all of my fans enjoy. And the director, Bobby Roast, is just a genius, an absolute genius. We make beautiful music together.

LEAFY SCENE: What everybody wants to know, Ms. Broccoli—

BIANCA: Call me Bianca, dear, please.

LEAFY SCENE: What everybody wants to know, Bianca, is how you got started fighting crime, on top of everything else you do! It sounds exhausting.

BIANCA: Well, you know, I am in the Green Box League of Nutritious Justice. This was the idea of three fabulous rock stars in their own right, the delicious superheroes Knute Trition, the tasteful Ed Yucation, and the spicy Ms. X. R. Cise.

LEAFY SCENE: Yes ...

BIANCA: And they came to visit me one day — I had just finished teaching a class of the most delightful young singers — and they said, "Bianca, darling, help us to save the world." So what should I do? I said yes, of course. And now, in addition to my performing and teaching and charities, I have this.

LEAFY SCENE: And you go around fighting the bad guys? O.B.C.D., Cole Esteorl, Di A. Betes, and all those villains? That's up your alley?

BIANCA: It's not exclusively fighting, with the fists and feet. I'm happy to say that it's easy to make a difference in the world by doing what you do best, if it helps people. I like to help people, you know. I lower cholesterol and detoxify the body, to keep things running smoothly and in natural harmony.

LEAFY SCENE: You said in a recent interview that you help people avoid lifestyle diseases.

BIANCA: Yes, darling, for who has time to get sick? Stick with me — is this the microphone? Am I on camera? — Stick with me, darlings, and you'll live longer and have more fun doing it. Parents, doctors, and anyone who really cooks know this to be true. I mix it up as a crime fighter, but I do it my way, on my terms. And I get results.

LEAFY SCENE: Bianca, you're a sparkling green gem. Thank you for doing everything you do for us, and thank you for taking the time to speak with me today.

BIANCA: Darling, any time. Life is to be lived as a flower, you know? Look at me. I am open to the world, and I believe so much in being the best you can be. Go out and sing, my darlings. But only do me a favor: not with your mouth full. Chew and swallow, darlings; that's Bianca's advice. Then sing!

Spell Me

Bianca

COLOR US!

The chamber door opened, a cloud of mist billowed out, and with dozens of reporters and scientists waiting in eager anticipation, a thrilling and familiar sound emerged: "Yee-ha!" Then Blueberry Bill himself popped out, twirling his lariat and smiling his confident smile. "Dadgum! We did it, fellers!"

This was amazing! The mob of happy figures pressed in, clamoring for information, for details, for stories of the trip, but Bill held them off with a hand in the air, and waited a moment. Then he spoke.

"Now, boys, it is true that I have returned from my adventures back in time, and I can confirm that it is just as wondrous and exotic there as our probes have suggested. I have seen dinosaurs and knights and pirates, and danced with princesses and dodged falling meteorites and even housetrained a saber-toothed tiger, but before I go on a step further, I have to ask: where-all is my grandson? I do miss the lad."

And with that, Percy Peach was allowed to step through the crowd, and he was wearing his baseball uniform and was oh-so proud of his adventuresome grandfather.

"Papa Bill! You made it! What was it like?" he beamed.

Now Blueberry Bill was happy to rest, and he was offered a chair and sat in it, and Percy hopped up on his lap. And this was what Bill told everybody:

"As fantastic as those other eras were, there is one thing true that never changes, and that is our need every day in every way to take good care of our bodies, minds, and spirit. We have to be ready for anything at any time, because you never know what new direction life is gonna take you."

Percy looked up at his grandfather with pride.

"Now, take me, for instance. I've got one of the highest antioxidant capacities among all fruits, vegetables, spices, and seasonings, and so I fight off harmful free radicals that could make us sick. And they've got free radicals back in time as sure as they abound today, and will tomorrow."

Photographers snapped Bill's picture as he spoke.

"I dare any one of you to take a trip like I just did without the optimum in brain health! My memory's sharp, and though I'm clearly blue, I'm by no means depressed about nothin'. Blueberries can do it all and then some."

A reporter interrupted. "Are you saying only blueberries can go back in time?"

Bill didn't like being interrupted, but he understood the young man's exuberance.

"Not at all, not at all. My point is that anyone can do fantastic things, if they've the will and smarts — and support — to live the right way. Why, look at my grandson, Percy. Nothin' particularly blueberry about him, on account of what's he's blessed with on his momma's side."

Percy smiled for the photographers, whose cameras clicked in rapid succession.

Bill continued:

"Just as I roamed the past, it's boys and girls like Percy who belong to the future. Look at this good ol' boy: fuzzy and soft, sure; but don't let that fool you. He's bursting with vitamins and minerals — you got your vitamin A, C, E, and K, along with thiamin, riboflavin, vitamin B-6, niacin, folate, and potassium — all of which contribute to healthy vision, blood pressure, and bones. This boy's all about good health."

Percy spoke up: "Plus we're high in fiber and promote healthy digestion and colon health, and even help ward off cancer and cardiovascular disease!"

Bill beamed at his grandson. "You got that right, slugger. So you see, fellas, it ain't so much what life gives you, it's what you bring out from the inside. You make your own destiny."

Then he stood up. Percy held Bill's hand as they made their way toward the lab door, and the great outdoors.

"Is that all? Can't you stay for questions? What about the dinosaurs and princesses!" shouted the reporters.

"Later, fellers," Bill said with a smile. "The past ain't goin' nowhere. Right now I'm right on time to see my peach of a grandson pitch in the big ball game. And that's an adventure I'm pleased as punch I'm here for."

Brian Bison was the best player on his school's basketball team, the All-naturals. Today he played all 20 minutes of the first half, posting a team-high 12 points with three assists and two steals.

If you don't know what that means, it's OK. Just take it from us: he plays hard and pretty darn well.

Now it was half time, the game was tied, and the All-naturals were drinking water while Coach Stringbein explained his strategy for the second half.

"OK, they're playing with a point guard and two wing players — 3-out, 2-in — so let's try a 1-2-2 trapping zone," the coach began. All the guys watched him intently, nodding.

Everyone but Brian Bison. He was distracted by something he saw at the other end of the court, where the opposing team was receiving instructions from their coach.

"Bison! You with us?" Coach Stringbein said.

Brian only dimly heard this. He watched with wide eyes as the opposing players' star, Burton Turtle, receiving orders from his coach, was popping the top off a red soft drink can, and preparing to take a sip. And there, off to the right, up in the stands, an old foe wrung his hands and cackled gleefully.

"Bison!"

"Excuse me, Coach. There's something I've got to do."

While Coach Stringbein and all of Brian's teammates watched, Brian broke ranks, ran down the court to the opposing team's bench, and interrupted the proceedings.

"Bison? What are you doing here?" This was Coach Oregano, from the visiting team.

"I know I'm not supposed to be here, and I'm sorry to interrupt, but look."

And he pointed to the stands where a six-foot-tall bottle of purple liquid fizzed angrily. It was wearing a sweater with the home team's school colors, hoping to blend in with the crowd.

"What the—" began Coach Oregano. "Who let Di A, Betes in here?"

"Exactly," said Brian, now looking at Burton Turtle, who was so surprised by the commotion he'd forgotten to take a sip from the can still raised to his lips.

"Turtle!" shouted the coach. "Don't drink that!"

"I … I …" stammered the player. "This was water! I know it was! Somebody must have switched it on me!"

The crowd roared in surprise. Nothing like this had ever happened before, where a player from one team would go out of his way to help a player from another team.

"Thanks, Brian," said Burton Turtle. "All that sugar, those empty calories … I owe you one."

Brian looked for the menacing Di A, Betes in the stands, but the foe had slipped away during the excitement.

"That's OK, Burt. I know you'd do the same for me."

"You're a hero, kid: a real hero," said Coach Oregano. And it was true: Brian was a member of the Green Box League of Nutritious Justice. He also enjoyed playing school sports, and didn't want to think of himself as a celebrity.

On his walk back to the All-naturals' bench

amid thunderous cheers, Brian thought about the compliment: a real hero. But is just plain doing the right thing heroic? He preferred to think he was just being a friend and a good guy. Anyone could do that.

Brian Bison's team went on to win the game, by the way, and the next one as well.

THE GREEN BOX LEAGUE OF

NUTRITIOUS JUSTICE

Spell Me

Brian ＿ ＿ ＿ ＿ ＿ ＿

With Knute Trition and Ed Yucation out of the way on their Earth to take midterm exams, and X. R. Cise kept busy at the marina by Salty Snake and the Sugar Shark, O.BC.D. knew the time was right to strike a helpless populace. In his laboratory he stepped into a trash-littered chamber, pressed a peppermint button, and —

Nothing happened.

Munching a candy bar in annoyance, he thought through the steps again: exams, diversion, chamber, button, lever … Aha! He hadn't pulled the lever! Now down came the lever, which looked like a giant submarine sandwich with a bite taken out of it. Fierce energies crackled; a mournful wind howled out of nowhere; lightning struck; O.BC.D. was seized by an overpowering urge to fart, which he did! Ah-ha-ha! And then …

He grew! Ten, twenty, fifty feet tall, rising out of an opening in his laboratory roof. He was enormous in his pudding-like countenance: pink and glossy, with giant French fries draped across his body, and dropping fast-food wrappers now akin to king-sized bed sheets. He grew and grew until his extra bulk barely squeezed through the open roof, and he stepped out into the night.

"Wheeze!" he wheezed, and it was a terrible sound.

And then, swallowing hard, and with grim purpose, set out for town to cause trouble. All that night and into the next he reigned, stealing healthy foods and replacing them with packaged items plump with refined sugars and chemical preservatives; he rained fats down upon the land.

In his wake were pools of butter; what he touched turned to junk food.

In town there was panic. Where was Knute? Where was Ed? Where was Xandra? Nobody knew. Someone would have to take this guy down.

"And that somebody is us," Brutus Beef told a small group of friends gathered at the school gym: Chucky Chicken, Petey Pork, Samantha Seafood, and Tabitha Turkey. "It's like the League always says, 'If you can change something for the best, and nobody else will — or can — step up and change it, then it's your job, sometimes, to be that person,'" Brutus said.

"But how do we take down O.BC.D. all by ourselves?" asked Chucky. "Have you seen how overgrown he is? We'll need help!"

"That's just it, kid, there is no one else right now," Brutus said. "You're right: although what we bring to the game is essential — all-natural, lean animal protein and essential amino acids — to finish the job we're going to need help from carbohydrates and water and sleep and fruits and vegetables."

Samantha Seafood, in her bubble of water, took it from there: "Brutus is right. If we can slow O.BC.D. down, even for a little while, we can buy time for the others to get into position. I know that's what Knute would recommend. Let's do this."

Petey Pork found his resolve, too, saying, "For our friends. We just can't let them get heart disease, type 2 diabetes, obstructive sleep apnea, certain types of cancer, and osteoarthritis, if we can help it. This is our time to shine."

Following a trail of destruction, they found O.BC.D. — under attack! Brian Bison already

96

had him down and was trampling the creature; X. R. Cise, fresh from victory at the marina, was keeping Obie off his feet with a barrage of heavy medicine balls. Brutus, Chucky, Petey, Samantha, and Tabitha joined the fray, and soon Obie was sweating gravy — and done for.

(He was lazy and a bully, and couldn't bear it when people stood up for themselves.)

"I give up! Quit it! No more!" Obie complained.

"Not so fast," Xandra said. "Let's see some push-ups. Give me five good push-ups, and then we'll know you've stopped your attack."

Obie turned over and did his best to comply. With each push-up he lost weight and enormous size. Push-ups were difficult to do well at first, but they came easier. Obie lost count and actually did seven push-ups, and soon was his normal size — which was still too big, but it was a start.

"All right, you did your best," Xandra said. "Let's have no more trouble out of you." And Obie took off for his lab, grumbling about lean protein, and not sure of his next steps.

The friends let out a cheer. It was good to stand up for each other, and it felt great to beat the bad guy.

Soon the town was cleaned up and it was business as usual.

After dinner, Knute emerged with a flash

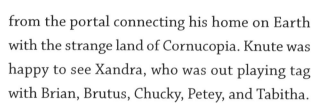

from the portal connecting his home on Earth with the strange land of Cornucopia. Knute was happy to see Xandra, who was out playing tag with Brian, Brutus, Chucky, Petey, and Tabitha.

"Hi, Xandra. I hated to be away so long. Did I miss any adventures?" he said.

Xandra thought for a moment. "Just the same old stuff: friends helping friends. Glad you're back."

Then Knute felt a swish of water and a swift kiss on the cheek. It was Samantha Seafood, who'd joined the game.

"Tag, you're it!" she said. And she swam away almost as fast as Knute could chase her.

No one on the Green Box League of Nutritious Justice knew how Bubba Black-Eyed Pea managed to help so many people and take down so many villains day after day. Some said it was his soluble fiber, which helps prevent type 2 diabetes and heart disease.

Other said it was his ample magnesium, calcium, and iron that did the trick.

Still others said it must have been his seemingly boundless reserves of the antioxidants vitamin A and manganese, which help keep the immune system strong.

Bubba was modest.

"I'm just lucky, I guess," he said.

And it was true, he was lucky: no one else on the League seemed to be in just the right place at just the right time to help out as often.

Knute was teaching Bubba how to fly one day. They were up in the thinnest, highest reaches of the sky, looking down on the great green, brown, and blue Earth. Fields, cities, and mountains rolled off into the distance, dropping away over the horizon.

Bubba spotted something.

"Be right back, Knute," he said.

"Do you want company?" Knute asked.

"No, thanks. I'm good." And he peeled off and rocketed away to the south.

Knute circled for a few minutes. It was a nice day to fly. What errand could Bubba be on? After a few minutes of enjoying airborne somersaults and cartwheels, Knute finally saw a small dot arcing up through scattered clouds to meet him. It was Bubba, smiling his quiet, modest smile.

"OK, all set," Bubba said, and the two friends flew on.

"What was that all about?" Knute finally asked.

"My detour? Oh, nothing much. I just saw a platoon of our guys in the military in the mood for a filling ham and black-eyed peas dinner, but who were short of ingredients. I hooked them up," he said.

Knute looked back. It all looked like farms and fields to him. "That's incredible. How do you find these amazing ways to help?"

Bubba winked at him. "Just lucky, I guess."

COLOUR US!

103

A chase that began in New York City and hopscotched the United States by plane, train, and automobile now seemed destined to end on a cruise ship approaching the white sandy beach of Waikiki, Honolulu, on the south shore of the island of Oahu, Hawaii.

The villain Di A. Betes, purple with exertion and starting to fizz, stood on the bow of the lavish Pacific Buffet holding a life preserver and a ray gun. He was going to jump.

"I'll make it back to my tropical lair, and then I'll regroup! And there ain't nothing you 'heroes' can do to stop me! All the world will one day feel the wrath of my insulin inhibitor, and then, heh heh heh, you'll all have excessive levels of glucose in your blood, and eventually type 2 diabetes!"

Penelope Pineapple and Candace Coconut,

in pursuit of the fiend since they'd spotted him giving kids liters of soda to drink at the dinner table way back on the East Coast, didn't want him to slip through their fingers. They let him keep talking while they moved toward him carefully.

A crowd of cruise ship revelers watched the scene unfold.

Addressing them, Di A. Betes continued:

"You're all helpless against me! Soon you'll all crave saturated fat, fatty animal protein, simple carbohydrate, and over-processed vegetables. Not a man, woman, or child among you will prefer far healthier, and more filling, plant and grain products or lean, all-natural meat protein. Nobody prefers easily digestible and nutrient-rich food choices anyway! Ha ha ha!"

"You're wrong!" a child in the crowd stepped forward to shout.

"We know what we need to live well, and have lots of energy, and grow big and strong! And it isn't you!"

Candace Coconut had to smile. There were new superheroes emerging all the time.

The child continued:

"You're just jealous! You'll never be as good as the Green Box League of Nutritious Justice, and you know it! All you do is make people sick and have to go to the hospital! And my dad says you make health care and insurance way too costly for America to afford!"

Di A. Betes smiled.

"Yes, precisely, that's my plan! Would you like a candy bar for being so astute?" And indeed he pulled a candy bar out from a little bag of treats he carried, and waved it forward.

Bad move.

Before Candace could take him down with her coconut water (rich in healthy fats that have been shown to help the brain function at its best and aid in weight loss and hormone regulation for both blood sugar and thyroid management), and before Penelope could hit him with her manganese and bromelain (known to help proper digestion and afford possible cancer protection), the crowd of seagoing vacationers roared — and charged Di A. Betes, hauling him down to the deck of the ship, and shaking him up something fierce.

"Should we help the poor sap?" Candace asked Penelope.

"I suppose so," Penelope replied. "Maybe when we dock, or the day after that."

THE GREEN BOX LEAGUE OF NUTRITIOUS JUSTICE

Spell Me

Candace

_ _ _ _ _ _ _

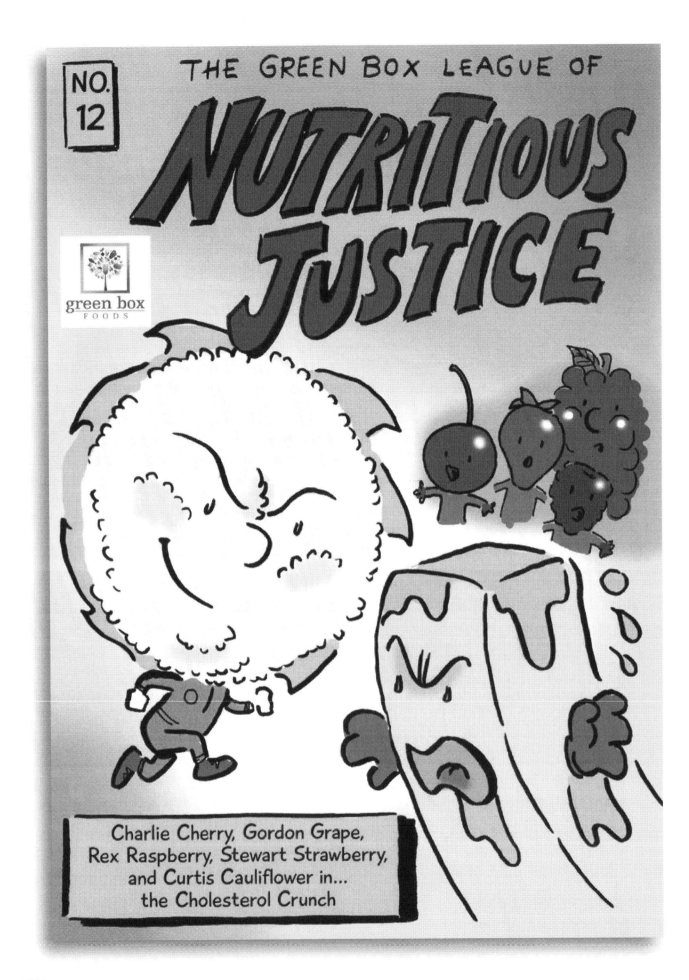

Our bodies make cholesterol, which is a good thing. This waxy, fat-like substance helps us live: it's always helping our cells take care of us. It even converts sunlight into vitamin D for us, and insulates nerve fibers so we can think, feel, and move well.

But a little goes a long way.

Cole Esterol, a short, stocky, sticky little waddly guy, didn't believe in a little going a long way. He believed in a lot going too far.

"More cholesterol, more!" he mused from the comfort of his oversized doughnut. "People have to know I was there!" And he thought about how to slip extra slick, fatty gunk into people's diet without them or the Green Box League of Nutritious Justice finding out.

He knew that when too much cholesterol is present, plaque — a thick, hard deposit — forms in the body's arteries, narrowing the space for blood to flow to the heart or brain. Over time, this buildup causes atherosclerosis, a hardening of the arteries, which can lead to heart disease.

He wrote that down on his to-do list: heart disease.

Moreover, he knew, when not enough oxygen-carrying blood reaches the heart, chest pain can result. And if the blood supply to a portion of the heart is completely cut off by total blockage of a coronary artery? The result is a heart attack.

When a blood clot blocks an artery or vein, interrupting the flow to an area of the brain? A stroke results, resulting in sometimes-severe permanent damage to the brain.

That evening, with darkness gathering, Cole slipped out of his lair, checked his to-do list, and headed into town on his motor scooter. A helmet covered his squishy little head. He was laughing.

Curtis Cauliflower was on patrol. Shadowing him were Charlie Cherry, Gordon Grape, Rex Raspberry, and Stewart

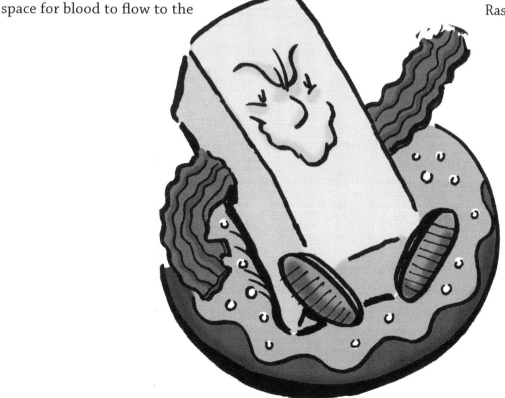

Strawberry. They were playful, pointing out opposites: "We're fruits; you're a vegetable; we're small, you're large; we're colorful, you're white."

"Quiet, you guys," Curtis said.

Rumor had it Cole Esterol was seen promoting foods high in saturated fats: red fatty meats, some pies, sausages, hard cheese, lard, pastry, cakes, most biscuits, cream, you name it. He was up to something. Curtis could all but smell it.

"OK, here's what we'll do," he told his partners. "Fan out. See who's not getting enough exercise and is just sitting around. Find all the people with excess body weight and the obese. Make note of the smokers and people who drink too much alcohol."

"Eew!" the berries and grapes said.

"I know. But these are the victims, most likely, of high 'bad' cholesterol and low 'good' cholesterol. From there we'll find out where Cole is getting his stuff, and we'll shut him down."

Gordon knew this from the Green Box Foods website:

"Low-density lipoprotein (LDL) is the bad kind, and high-density lipoprotein (HDL) is the good kind. Too much LDL in the bloodstream can build up on the walls of the arteries that lead to the heart and the brain; HDL carries cholesterol away from the arteries and back to the liver, where it's processed and sent out of the body — and might even help remove cholesterol from

wherever plaque has taken hold," he said.

"Got it," Charlie, Rex, and Stewart said. They knew all this, of course, but Gordon was a good guy and liked to help.

They split up and began their search. And everyone around the world was happy to see the berries and grapes, as these are always so tasty and full of vitamins and antioxidants. The heroes met back in an hour.

"Well?" asked Curtis.

"We're in luck," Gordon said. And they filled him in on what they'd seen.

Cole was waiting at the hospital, eager to gloat over the arrival of his many victims of foods high in saturated fats. But he was in for a surprise.

"You!" he said.

There would be no human victims that night.

Instead, looming over Cole Esterol were Curtis and the other heroes of the Green Box League of Nutritious Justice.

"How did you find me?"

"Give it up, Cole. We educated everyone about what you've been up to. There's no future in saturated fats, and we got people to rethink smoking and excessive alcohol. You're finished."

But Cole Esterol had one more trick up his sleeve. He charged right at Curtis, low to the ground and fast. He wanted revenge.

Curtis smiled. He'd been expecting this.

Cole whammed into Curtis with all his might, hoping to topple the strong vegetable. But Curtis didn't budge, and Cole … vanished.

"Where'd he go? What happened? Who turned out the lights?" the berries asked.

"Come on, guys: this way to the jailhouse."

"But where is he? What happened?" asked a startled Gordon.

"You tell me, you're so smart. What do you know about cauliflower?"

Gordon thought for a moment.

"Cauliflower is part of the cruciferous vegetable family, which has health benefits above and beyond those of mere ordinary vegetables: detoxification; antioxidants, which protect our cells against cancer formation; anti-inflammation; heart health, and digestive support," he said.

"And?" Curtis prompted?

"And they're potent weapons against obesity and type 2 diabetes, and ..."

Now he had remembered.

"They naturally keep cholesterol levels down. You mean ..."

"That's right. I ate him. But don't worry. I'll be dropping him off where he can't do anybody any more harm."

THE GREEN BOX LEAGUE OF
NUTRITIOUS JUSTICE

Spell Me
Gordon
_____

t was love at first sight: Celine Celery and Cosmo Cucumber.

She with her cool and crisp bearing, brimming with plant-based antioxidant nutrients such as vitamin C, beta-carotene, and manganese; he with his large water volume and shared wealth of vitamin C, beta-carotene, and manganese.

"Oh, Cosmo! How I adore that you fight cardiovascular disease and several cancer types!"

"Oh, Celine, my love, how you thrill me by protecing against unwanted oxygen damage to the cells, blood vessels, and organ systems, and benefitting the digestive and cardiovascular systems!"

They gazed into each other's eyes and held hands.

This lovely-dovey stuff was all too much for O.BC.D., whom these heroes had just caught red-handed making kids too doughy to climb a tree. They'd walloped him good and hauled him before the judge, in whose chambers they all stood.

"Your honor, I'm guilty, guilty! Lock me away. But only please — send me as far from these lovebirds as possible!"

You see, Obie was excessively sweet. But he was hardly romantic. 🌿

THE GREEN BOX LEAGUE OF

NUTRITIOUS JUSTICE

Spell Me

Celine _____

Knute Trition was flying high above the Earth, chasing a giant pink cupcake, bobbing and weaving between the clouds. The cupcake, in desperation, shot gobs of pink frosting backwards to throw Knute off the trail.

Knute dodged them easily.

"Give it up, Obie, there's no escape!" Knute shouted. "I caught you red-handed — er, pink-handed — lulling those bank guards to sleep. Surrender!"

The fiendish blob of sweets and fats named O.BC.D. was getting winded. He knew he couldn't keep up the pace. Maybe he could make it to his hideout at the waterfront.

"Never! So what if I was trying to break into the food bank! There's no law against it," he called back. O.BC.D. had only wanted to make a slight withdrawal after hours: just a million dollars, for candy.

Knute saw they were over the water now, deep and blue. What was the cupcake's plan? Never mind: he had one of his own. Edging closer to the wheezing pastry, he grabbed at his wide blue foil "pants" and pulled.

O.BC.D., stripped of his cup, suddenly lost control and tumbled to the water, shedding French fries and cookies as he fell. He landed with a cannonball splash. Then he surfaced, flailing helplessly.

"Help! Help!" he shouted. "I never learned to swim!"

High above, Knute had stopped to fold the villain's foil cup. He should throw it in the trash, he thought, but it was evidence. And now there was the matter of the sinking creep below. But if his timing was right ...

...and it was! There was a flash of orange below, approaching the stricken cupcake. It was Connor Carrot in his scuba gear, out exploring a shipwreck.

Connor surfaced and snagged the limp cupcake by an onion ring, saving it from a watery grave.

"Hello, Knute!" he called. "What's the idea polluting the ocean?"

Knute flew down.

"Thanks, Connor. I'll take it from here. This guy needs to answer to a judge," Knute said.

"Oh, I get it. Well, he's all yours. I'm heading back down to look for gold and emeralds."

"Have fun," said Knute. "Sorry to interrupt the excursion."

"Not at all," Connor said. "Haven't you heard? Carrots are great against inflammation, in the body or out at sea. We like when things go comfortably. So I'm happy to help any time!"

Now Knute lugged the heavy cupcake above the waves and was flying him back to shore, where police were waiting.

"I would have gotten away with it, too, if not for you and your orange friend back there," O.BC.D. grumbled.

Nothing the villain said would have surprised Knute. This bad guy seldom made sense.

"Be that as it may, Obie, but you owe your life to that carrot. Never forget: it helps to have friends in low places."

THE GREEN BOX LEAGUE OF
NUTRITIOUS JUSTICE

Spell Me

Connor ___ ___ ___ ___ ___ ___

Enzo Eggplant, Pierre Potato, Barry Beet, and Gary Garlic were lying out, covered in oil, and soaking up the rays.

"This is the life, eh, fellas?" said Enzo.

"Boy, you said it," agreed Pierre. It had been too long since they had been able to just relax and unwind. Being a superhero kept them all busy most of the time.

Whether it was Enzo saving the city from the rampaging Carb Crab; Pierre safely capturing all those escaped chocolate chimps; Barry squaring off against the giant Juice Moose (in a battle that raged for a week); or Gary helping save the whole Green Box League of Nutritious Justice from O.BC.D. and his army of Processed Parasites, it was always something.

"And now this," Enzo observed.

"What?" said Pierre.

"Does that seem like something we should take care of, or should we let it slide?"

High in the sky, and now edging out the Sun, was a giant blimp: O.BC.D.'s special zeppelin, from which the madman was throwing tons and tons of fast food, all of which began striking rooftops, porches, and streets with sickening splats.

"What is this guy's deal?" said Barry.

No matter. In a flash, all four heroes had their League uniforms on and were rocketing to work:

Pierre, packed with power, smashed Obie's blimp.

Enzo, beaming a proud, glossy purple, hauled a squawking Obie out of his pilot seat, rescuing him, and tossed him over to Barry.

Barry, armed with the phytonutrients betalain and vulgaxanthin, and an expert at providing antioxidant, anti-inflammatory, and detoxification support, dragged Obie and his shredded blimp to police headquarters.

And Gary, once again protecting against heart disease and type 2 diabetes, swept the streets and rooftops clear of Obie's offending empty calories.

Soon the heroes were back on their chairs and relaxing under sunny skies.

"This is the life, eh, fellas?" said Enzo.

"Boy, you said it," agreed Pierre.

They'd been fighting for a week: the bad guys with ham grenades, cholesterol bombs, and eat-seeking missiles; and the good guys with almost everything in their arsenal, including breakfast potato blasts, superstar scramblers, and Italian wedding soup.

"Maybe some more crunches would help," X. R. Cise offered.

"Or a classic three-hole punch," said Ed Yucation.

"A what?" said Knute Trition.

"Paperwork joke," admitted Ed.

Knute thought for a moment.

"In a case like this, when we're pinned down, it's time to bring out the big guns."

"You don't mean ..." said X. R. Cise.

"You couldn't possibly ..." started Ed Yucation.

"Precisely," said Knute. And he placed an emergency call.

Two minutes later a dark shadow crossed over the battlefield and then there was a moment of anticipation. They were beautiful: Gary Garlic and Gina Ginger flew overhead, heading directly for the forces of obesity, diabetes, hypertension, and cholesterol. And then they let loose.

When the first explosions of good health rang out, all the heroes of the Green Box League of Nutritious Justice let out an enormous cheer. The tide had turned! Blast after blast of high energy, strong muscles, and alert thinking had saved the day! Now the heroes could move in and sweep up.

When all was said and done, a beaten and battered O.BC.D. admitted, "I never saw it coming. What on Earth did they hit us with?"

Knute was there, raising the heroes' flag.

"That was Gary Garlic, whom you might have smelled coming. I don't want to tell you all of his secrets, but you have no defense against how he helps blood vessels expand, which keeps blood pressure in check."

Cole Esterol, now in handcuffs, added: "Garlic packs a punch, boss. All that vitamin C, vitamin B-6, selenium, and manganese? Devastating. That guy lowers blood triglycerides and total cholesterol levels — so he protects against heart disease and type 2 diabetes."

Gina Ginger was wiping her hands after the battle. "Don't forget me, boys: I kicked your butts too. More than a delicacy and a spice, I'm flat-out medicinal. I'm anti-inflammatory all the way, so the good guys feel better and live longer!"

"Her smell and taste," said Cole. "Fantastic, but so strong!"

"Take 'em away, boys," Knute said, and the villains were carted off to face justice. Green Box League of Nutritious Justice.

Knute wished all life's battles could wrap up so easily.

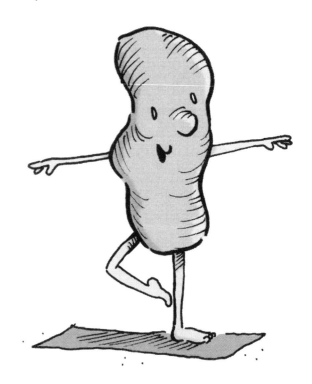

Mail call at the Green Box League of Nutritious Justice!

Today a letter came postmarked Camp Sunnyside, where Gregory Grapefruit and Hillary Honeydew are spending the summer. Xandra opened the envelope, pulled the letter out, and read it to all of Gregory and Hillary's friends, who had gathered to hear. It said,

Dear fellow superheroes,

We are having the most amazing time at camp! Gregory loves archery, fishing, kayaking, hiking, and arts and crafts. I love badminton, horseback riding, painting, and also hiking and arts and crafts. We are staying in different cabins. Mine is all girls, and his is all boys. Some of the kids are our age, and some are older. A few are younger. We are the only ones who look like we do, but that's fine, because we're superheroes.

Gregory got in trouble two days ago because he was flying, like *really* super fast around the lake, and the counselors said we're not supposed to fly at all because nobody else here can fly even a foot. I think that's a silly rule. Gregory's OK. He's not upset. He didn't have to apologize or anything, just say he wouldn't do it again.

I made a friend. Her name is Tess. Her father is an accountant and her mother is a teacher. She has a baby brother named Jacob. Tess and I are best friends at camp, and are the two best badminton players. There's going to be a big games day at the end of summer, and Tess and I are going to enter all the contests together. Gregory will too, I think.

The food here is good, but not as good as it is back at League headquarters. The kitchen is very neat and tidy, which is nice to see, and we eat a variety of plant-based and lean-meat protein, and get our carbohydrates from low-sugar fruits and non-starchy vegetables. There are more starchy carbs, like bread, rice, and potatoes, than I would like, and I let the camp director know that even though they're offering whole grains, these will drive up blood sugars more than fruits and vegetables would.

The camp director is a very nice man named Mr. Pleasance. He said, "Thank you, Hillary, I will contact the meals director about this."

Gregory just came in and told me that he finished his big crafts project: it's a fully operational M1A2 Abrams tank made entirely out of pinecones, construction paper, Popsicle sticks, school glue, rubber bands, birch bark, and composite armor. I told him he should glue glitter on it, but he said no. "Come on, Gregory, please!" He still said no. That boy is stubborn.

Then he jumped in and started it up. You should see him race around!

Each of the kayaks at the lake has a name. There's Dolphin, Minnow, Perch, Willy, Sea Breeze, and Islander. I like Sea Breeze the best because it's turquoise, which is my favorite color — and Tess's too.

Now there is a big commotion outside.

I just checked: there is a giant, colossal, huge, cobalt blue alien octopus or something running around the camp, and everyone is scared. Gregory is in his tank. He's not scared. You should see him! Even his helmet is made out of pinecones, which would look awesome if they glittered. Gregory's tank engine is loud.

Tonight for sharing I will tell everyone all about the Green Box League of Nutritious Justice and the role I play in it. I will tell them that I have sweet, greenish flesh; am a rich source of potassium, which helps manage and prevent high blood pressure; and that my vitamin C boosts the immune system. I'm proud that my B vitamins get rid of toxins and can prevent Alzheimer's and heart disease.

Oh, did you feel that? You couldn't, because this is a letter. The giant octopus thing is shooting missiles all-around. It runs so fast and skitters! It planted a flag on the volleyball court, but

Gregory knocked it down. Why would it put its flag on our volleyball court? I don't understand alien monsters.

There goes Gregory, driving after the thing! Whoosh, whoosh, whoosh go the pinecones. He should just fly up and punch the creature in the nose, but he promised not to fly.

Sorry, I've just been watching the battle. Gregory is having so much fun!

I told him this morning he should tell about himself for sharing, but I think he wants to talk about baseball or something. He plays baseball here at camp just like at home.

Before I started writing to you I wrote out something for Gregory to say in sharing if he changes his mind about baseball:

"I am Gregory Grapefruit, a large citrus fruit with a bitter yellow rind and inner skin and a highly flavored, somewhat acid, juicy pulp. I am a great source of vitamins A and C, which helps boost the immune system, specifically with inflammatory conditions such as asthma, osteoarthritis, and rheumatoid arthritis."

But knowing him he'll stick with baseball.

I also like that Gregory promotes cardiovascular health. That's one of my favorite things about him.

I just went outside to look around. All the counselors and campers are hiding. I walked right up to Gregory in his tank and told him he needed to stop playing with the alien octopus monster, and to get ready for sharing time. He asked me to feed in more pinecones, which I did, and then I reminded him to put glitter on the tank to make it look prettier.

He drove off without even saying thank you!

That's boys for you.

The tank is doing a good job, I have to admit. I'll send you a painting of it when I have time. It's really cool looking, and the alien doesn't like it at all.

Well, I can see that it's up to me to stop this battle because until I do, no one will be kayaking, playing badminton, swimming, or getting ready for share time. I'll have to fly up and bop it on the nose.

After all, I never promised I wouldn't fly.

I'll mail this after I stop the battle. I miss you all. I hope O.BC.D. isn't giving you a hard time. If he does, tell him he'll have to answer to Hillary Honeydew and Gregory Grapefruit when we get home.

Love,
Hillary

Enclosed in the letter was a painting, as promised, of Gregory's tank. It was shown parked on top of the alien octopus's head, which had Xs for eyes and a star rising from where its nose should be. That must have been where Hillary had bopped it.

130

Wally Watermelon was riding his bike at the boardwalk when he heard a cry for help. Trouble at the beach! After leaping over the rail, he bounded across the sand toward the crashing surf. There was a figure in the water signaling furiously.

"Are you OK? Hang on, I'm coming!" Wally yelled.

After kicking off his shoes and dumping his helmet, he waded into the warm water. When he got to the figure, who he'd been prepared to pull to safety, he saw not a frightened swimmer, but a full-grown shark — trailing lollipops, candy bars, jawbreakers, and peppermint sticks.

"Sugar Shark?"

"Ow, my teeth!" Sugar Shark complained. "I can't take it any longer. I need a dentist."

Wally was taken aback. Sugar Shark, one of the Legion of Unhealthy Injustice's most fearsome members, who loved nothing more than to see people chomp down on sugary foods and slurp up sweetened drinks, was asking for help.

"For real? You're really in pain?"

"Oh, agony! It started with one little toothache, but sharks have so many teeth, you see, and now it's worse. I can't eat and it even hurts to drink! Wally, I can't turn to O.BC.D. for help, as he likes to see everyone suffer — but you're one of the good guys. I need a dentist."

"OK, sure. There's one just a block away from

the beach. I'm sure he can see you. Come on. How do you ... Do you walk on your fins?"

"No, of course not, I'm a shark. You'll have to bring the dentist here. Please, Wally!"

By now a crowd had formed. Mothers pulled their small children close. Teens took pictures with their cell phones. It was an unusual sight for sure.

"OK. Stay calm. I'll go get the dentist."

"Thank you, thank you, thank you, Wally. Only please hurry!"

Dr. Mark Molare stood on the beach, perhaps 30 feet away from the stricken Sugar Shark. "It sounds like tooth decay and gum disease, but I'd have to examine him to be sure, and to recommend treatment," he said.

"Well, can you ... go in there and fix him up?" Wally asked.

"In the water? With a shark? To perform dentistry? It's out of the question. It doesn't sound safe for either of us. No, if you can get him to my examination room, then perhaps I can help. But sharks need to keep swimming to live, to extract oxygen from the water, so I don't know that that'll work either."

Sugar Shark moaned in discomfort.

Wally thought about it. Then he made a decision. He waded into the water.

"Look, Sugar Shark. There is someone who can help, but you have to promise to change your ways. All of these sugary treats you have around you all the time — it's adding to your problem. You did this to yourself, just as you continue to do it to billions of people worldwide. Refined sugar is everywhere, addictive, and poisonous."

"And," interjected Dr. Molare, "as your friend here knows, in addition to painful tooth decay, refined sugar leads to obesity, cardiovascular disease, diabetes, and non-alcoholic fatty liver disease."

"I know, I know, I'm sorry now. I'll do anything," Sugar Shark said. "Who can help me, Wally?"

Wally patted the shark on the snout. He closed his eyes. He concentrated. Then he raised his arms, and in a clear, loud voice, said, "Water, water everywhere, to the rescue!"

A few moments later, the surf all-around them began flowing in a wide circle. There were no other swimmers in the area, as they were afraid of the shark. The water churned faster and faster, and then it spouted as a giant geyser that

134

formed a large human shape, with wind ruffling its wavy hair. Seagulls squawked at it at eye level, then flew away.

Looking down, the giant saw who had summoned it, and quickly melted down into a much smaller figure, just Wally's height, still made entirely of water, which sparkled in the afternoon sun refracting through it.

"Hey, Wally. What's up?" it said.

"H20, good to see you. Thanks for coming on such short notice."

Sugar Shark was speechless.

"I believe you know Sugar Shark, and this is Dr. Molare. He's a dentist."

"Nice to meet you, doctor. Hello, Sugar Shark. Not feeling well today, eh?"

The shark shook its head.

"Well, I'm not surprised. Look at all this junk you eat and drink."

And with that, H2O gathered all the shark's junk food and spun it into a waterspout, and launched it precisely into a trash can way off on the boardwalk.

Dr. Molare was impressed. "Nice shot, kid!"

"Thanks, Doc," H2O said. "I'm always amazed more people don't take advantage of the power of water. You pollute it out in the open with your industry, and you pollute your bodies with sugar, salt, saturated fats, and chemical stabilizers and preservatives. Do you not realize what your bodies are made of and what they need to survive?"

Sugar Shark shook his head again.

"Water is your body's main nutrient transport system. Without adequate water, the vitamins, minerals, and other nutrients you depend on essentially move through 'sludge.' All these juices, sodas, tea, coffee, and artificially sweetened sport beverages you drink aren't plain water, and are harmful. There's nothing simpler, easier, more abundant, and more healthy for you to drink than water," H2O said.

By now Sugar Shark was close to tears, or would be if sharks could cry.

"What about my teeth?"

"Well, fortunately, sharks replace their teeth pretty fast, unlike people, who only get one shot at it. But I can carry you to Dr. Molare's office and help you swim while he examines you. Will that be OK?"

"Yes, yes, anything ...."

Several days later Wally went to visit Sugar Shark at the beach again. The patient was in a much better mood, and trailed no candy or soft drinks.

"Wally, I can't thank you enough. I'm a new shark! It's nothing but sea lions and fish for me from now on. And, of course, water."

Wally smiled.

"That works for me! After all, I'm mostly water, and I feel great! And for anyone who prefers more flavoring, they can sweeten water naturally with sliced lemons, limes, or berries."

"You don't' recommend juices?"

"Not really. It's better to have the whole fruit or vegetable so that you get all the benefits of the whole food. Watermelon, for example, is a rich source of lycopene, key in controlling harmful lipids in the blood stream that otherwise might clog up the arteries. Other compounds can help improve blood flow, promote muscle recovery, spur healing, and deliver other aspects of cardiovascular health. Watermelon contains about 6 percent sugar and 91 percent water by weigh, so it's sweet, but naturally so. As with fruits generally, it is an abundant source of vitamin C."

"Dr. Molare recommended honey in the raw, which is approximately 50 percent fructose, but completely natural in its raw form and offering many health benefits when used in moderation, including a high antioxidant profile," the shark said.

"That's right," Wally agreed. "And Stevia, too, a highly sweet herb derived from the leaf of the South American stevia plant, which is completely safe in its natural form. There are much better options than refined sugar, as you've discovered."

Waving a fin goodbye, Sugar Shark — now considering a name change to Stevia Shark, or Steve, for short — turned toward the warm waters of the setting sun. It felt good to be alive.

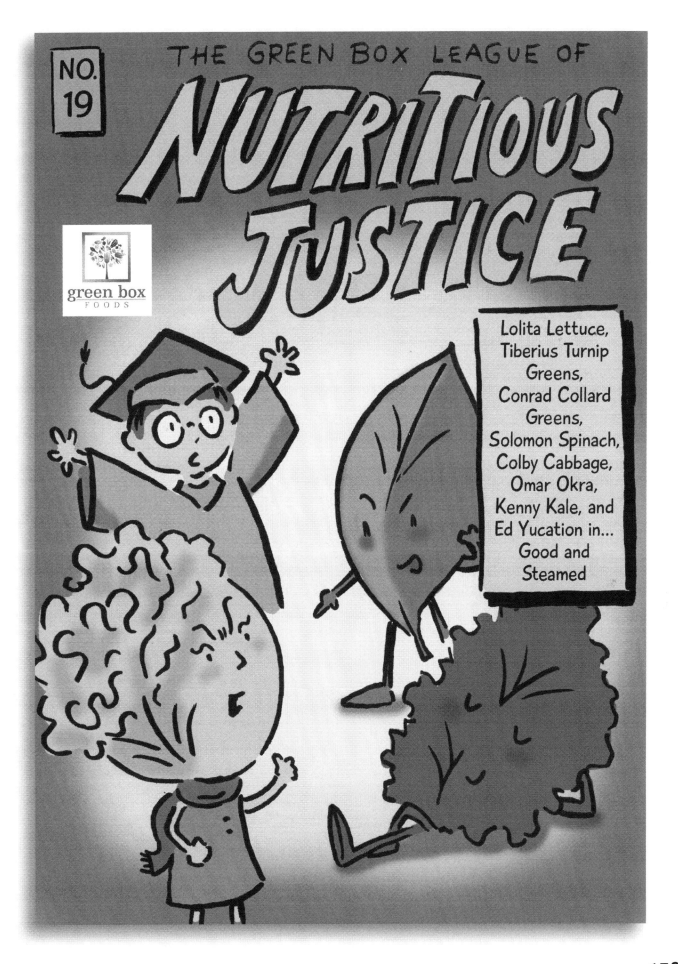

The sounds of arguing from within the Green Box League of Nutritious Justice were unusual. Ed Yucation hurried inside to see what was the matter. When he reached the League's kitchen, he was in for an earful.

"I am!"

"No, I am!"

"It's me!"

"I am!"

Ed tried to intervene, but Lolita Lettuce, Tiberius Turnip Greens, Conrad Collard Greens, Solomon Spinach, Colby Cabbage, and Omar Okra wouldn't have it.

"I'm the healthiest," argued Solomon Spinach.

"Everybody knows that. Strong to the finish, and all that!"

"No way, nuh-uh; it's Okra, baby; Okra all the way," countered Omar.

And, of course, Lolita, Tiberius, and Conrad fought on.

"Hey! Hey!" Ed finally said. "What's this all about? What started this?"

Omar jumped in: "One of us is the healthiest green. Just has to be. By process of elimination, bam bam bam, one of us has most of the numbers on his side. That's science, baby. And that's me."

That caused another flurry of arguing.

"People!" Ed shouted. The room grew quiet. "We have a major battle later today against

139

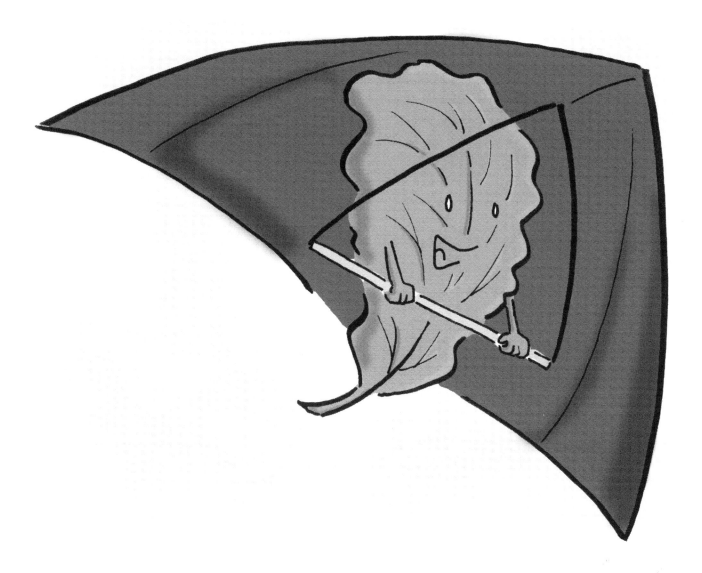

both diabetes and cancer. We can't afford to let squabbling distract us. We're all heroes. We are all here to do a job."

"But Eddie ..." began Omar.

"What got you started on this? One minute we're all happy as can be, and then this!"

Solomon walked up to the crime computer and pointed at the screen. "That. A report came in."

Ed read from the screen: "Greens are the number 1 food you can eat regularly to help improve your health. Leafy vegetables are brimming with fiber, vitamins, minerals, and plant-based substances that may help protect you from heart disease, diabetes, and perhaps even cancer."

Ed looked at the expectant faces around him.

"I don't understand. It says what we already know."

"Keep reading," Colby said.

Ed continued: "Even so, Americans are not eating as many vegetables each day as health experts recommend. To help readers load up on leafy goodness, we've ranked the country's most popular greens from most nutritious to least. Here's our top 10 list ..."

"Oh," he said. "Guys, whatever this says, just know that you're all valuable. Each of you. Every single one."

"It says Kenny Kale is most nutritious," Lolita said.

And in fact Kenny hadn't said a word since Ed arrived. He sat comfortably, leaning back in a chair, with his feet up on the table.

"Can't argue with perfection, yo. I'm a straight-up source of vitamins A, C, and K; I offer a good amount of calcium for a vegetable, and I supply folate and potassium. What else is there to say?"

That set off a new round of arguing.

"First of all, Ken, feet off the table. Second, as long as you wash your greens in a water-filled sink, drain the sink, then rinse again until the leaves are dirt-free, you can't go wrong. Any of you. You're all leafy greens."

He held back further shouting with a raised finger.

"No one loves figuring things out more than I do, and I respect that you're interested in research, but this is no way to settle anything. Shouting is a waste of time and energy. I'll get to the bottom of this."

After a few moments speed-reading the rest of the report, Ed was prepared to render a verdict.

"Kale: yes. I agree, but don't get cocky; turnip greens: you're a major-league leaf, but you'd do even better if you had the turnip too; mustard greens and broccoli, they're on assignment, but they weigh in at around 25 calories a serving and are rich in vitamins A and C, and potassium and folate."

Lolita waited for her name. She'd been on the verge of wilting.

"Red and green leaf and Romaine lettuce:

the darker the leaf, the more nutrition, so you're definitely dynamic. Don't give up. You're the go-to in salads, a job I seldom see kale volunteering for."

"Cabbage? You're pale but potent, especially for tonight's fight. My goodness: you're brimming with cancer-fighting compounds and vitamin C. In many ways you're the workhorse of the kitchen, and I've never known you to say you can't handle something."

Colby blushed.

"How about me, Ed?" said Solomon Spinach. "Where do I stand?"

"Solomon? Didn't I mention you?"

Solomon shook his head.

"You big galoot, did you know that you're amazing? When you're cooked, that's when your dietary calcium is freed up to fight crime. Mild mayhem, I call you. In soups, pasta dishes, and casseroles? Are you kidding me? Spinach all the way."

Everybody seemed pleased with Ed's report.

"Now let's put this behind us and load up for tonight. Hands together, come on."

And all the friends put their right hands together in a circle.

"Green Box League!" Ed began.

"Green Box League!" the others repeated.

"Of Nutritious!"

"Of Nutritious!"

"Justice!" Ed said.

"Justice!" the others repeated.

Ed didn't envy the enemy tonight. Those poor saps were going down hard, he could tell. 🌿

"Biff! Bam! Pow! Pucker up, crime; you're gonna get it right in the kisser!"

That was Lucy Lemon at the kitchen table, practicing her battle cry. Knute Trition, cooking dinner for several heroes at Green Box League of Nutritious Justice headquarters, was amused.

"Aren't you supposed to be doing your homework?"

"I am! I'm doing it!"

"Yelling, 'Biff, bam, pow' is part of your homework?"

"Sort of. Writing a short story is. I'm putting my battle cry in it as dialogue."

"Oh, I see," Knute said. "So it's very important that you shout."

"That's right: it's very important."

"By all means, continue. What's the story about?"

"Well," said Lucy, "it's about me and my most favorite superhero in the whole world. He's big and strong and handsome and I think he's the best ever."

Knute blushed. "You don't say," he said.

"Oh, yes. Why, he's the bravest and the smartest and the sweetest. You might think I prefer sour, in that I'm a lemon and have all this strong citric acid, which promotes the immune system and helps prevent cancer, but I don't! I really prefer sweet, and go well with it, and he's got it."

Knute stirred his pot. The sauce was rich and aromatic, and had been simmering for hours.

"Go on …"

"Well, it's about the time Hy Pertension tried to turn the whole Atlantic Ocean into yucky high-sodium soup, and we beat him up."

"I remember," Knute said.

"I was young then, and didn't have a battle cry. But if I had one, I would have yelled, 'Biff! Bam! Pow! Pucker up, crime; you're gonna get it right in the kisser!' Just like I said!"

"That would have been sweet."

The sauce was done. It was almost time for dinner.

"And I was there, and X. R. Cise was there, and you were there …"

"I remember," said Knute, beginning to smile. How to let the kid down easy …

"And Ed Yucation was there! Oh, he's so dreamy."

"Ed … You mean Ed is your favorite superhero?"

"Of course! He's got the loveliest brown eyes … Isn't he your favorite superhero too?"

"Um …"

"Oh, you probably can't say. It wouldn't be fair to everyone else."

"You know who my real favorite superhero is, Lucy? Right at this very moment?"

"Who?"

"It's you."

"It's me? Really?"

"Come on. Let's eat."

THE GREEN BOX LEAGUE OF

NUTRITIOUS JUSTICE

Spell Me

Lucy _ _ _ _ _ _ _

"Pizza with Malik Mushroom and Olivia Olive," read the invitation. "Come one, come all, and join us downtown at Mighty Pizza. It's on us!"

"How nice, a pizza party!" said Knute. "Guys, did you see this?"

Ed Yucation and X. R. Cise, the other two founding members of the League of Nutritious Justice, had their invitations as well.

"Pretty exciting," said Ed. "I haven't been to a pizza party in a long time. I've been so busy with school and sports, and of course keeping the world safe from the likes of the Legion of Unhealthy Injustice."

"The party starts in an hour," Xandra said. "Where are all the other members of the League? Should we round them up?"

Knute explored League headquarters to see if anybody else was free to go, but couldn't find the other heroes. He checked the game room, the crime lab, the kitchen, the giant robot test facility, the dormitory, the communications center, the gymnasium, the pool, the time travel chamber, the dinosaur pen, the inter-dimensional-portal landing pad, the library, the computer lab, the power plant, the biosphere, the gardens, the museum, the gallery, the awards showroom, the carport, the arcade, the band shell, the holographic zoo, the hot springs, the basement, the attic, the flight pad, and the observatory — all empty.

"That's odd," Ed said, and checked the grounds and the bounce house. Nothing.

"Weird," Xandra said, and peeked in at the art center and the auditorium. On a whim she looked in on the stockroom, compost, and recycling area. All deserted.

"Is it possible we're the last to know?" Knute wondered aloud.

"I've got a bad feeling about this," Ed said. "It's not like the guys to take off without letting us know. And we shouldn't leave headquarters unguarded."

"Do you think they're in trouble, Knute?" Xandra asked.

"Either that — or they're enjoying their pizza," Knute said.

ED STAYED BEHIND. Xandra and Knute flew off for downtown, looking for signs of trouble. When they reached Mighty Pizza, Knute peered through the roof and ceiling, and saw the League inside — all tied up as a group in an enormous loop of rope made out of French fries and deep-fried onion rings.

"O.BC.D.," said Xandra.

Knute nodded. "That overstuffed goon has gone too far this time. What do you say we dish out a little justice?"

But before either could take further action, they were struck with a strange yellow ray. They felt immediately overstimulated, and then fell to Earth. Captured by the bad guys! Unthinkable! But it was true.

BACK AT League headquarters, Ed watched the scene unfold by satellite video. As soon as he saw the ray strike Knute and Xandra, he fed his observations into the League computer. Analysis confirmed his worst fears.

He pressed a button on his console, and a red light flashed.

"Computer," he said. "Activate Smash Yucation."

INSIDE THE RESTAURANT, Knute, Xandra, and all the other heroes struggled against their bonds.

"Give it up, Noodlehead Knute; these are industrial-strength French fries, triple-reinforced with preservatives, saturated fats, and stabilizers. These don't biodegrade and they don't taste nearly as good as the real thing."

O.BC.D. stood with his hands on his wide hips, looking quite pleased.

Cole Esterol, Hy Pertension, and Di A. Betes chuckled behind him like the friends of a bully they were.

Sugar Shark, swimming in a big vat of black soda pop, grinned. He thrashed his tail in anticipation.

"The name's Knute Trition, Obie, and you've just made the biggest mistake of your chunky little life," Knute said.

"Oh, have I? Seems to me I've captured the entire Green Box League of Nutritious Justice! And the Sugar Shark is going to be well fed tonight. But where are Malik Mushroom and Olivia Olive? I want to thank them personally for throwing this party. When I heard it was going to be held here, it gave me the idea to crash your party with my own — and send you to your destruction!"

Malik and Olivia were five heroes away on Knute's left. And they were working on an escape. Just a few minutes more should do it.

"Well, no matter. I have you all," O.BC.D. said. "And with you out of the way, and my devastating

COMICS

150

High-Fructose Corn Syrup ray at the ready, the world is now my oyster! After all, if it can knock you out, it can knock out everybody! Whole armies! Kings! Nations!"

Obie was truly pleased. Pink frosting pooled around him, and jelly beans popped from his nose.

"That's all I wanted to hear, Obie," Knute said. "Thanks for telling us your plan, and what that ray is called. Hit it, Ed ..."

And with that signal, the entire roof of the restaurant lifted away, and stars shined down on a very surprised O.BC.D. There in the moonlight stood two hundred feet of the tallest, strongest, most determined robot the villain had ever seen. Battleship gray, it had Ed Yucation's features, with white headlight eyes — and it was smiling sweetly.

"The ray! The ray!" Obie shouted to Hy Pertension, who indeed swung the High-Fructose Corn Syrup ray projector up at the robot — and fired.

The projector bathed the robot in a sickly yellow glow. Then it dimmed. Nothing else had happened.

The robot, observing it was unharmed, then reached down and plucked O.BC.D. by the scruff, and raised him up to its eyes to study. Obie squirmed in fear. "Put me down! Please! I'm afraid of heights! Please, Mr. Yucation."

The robot complied. It settled Obie down in the soda pop waters, where the Sugar Shark set to work on its sudden meal. The waters bubbled and foamed.

Just then Malik and Olivia snapped the cables holding all the heroes. They were free, and all let out an enormous cheer.

All of the other villains ran in terror, but they were caught and tied in ropes of their own invention.

BACK AT HEADQUARTERS, the heroes finally got to enjoy the pizza party they'd been looking forward to. Even the robot was there, sitting on its haunches and squeezing into the dining room as best it could. (But even so it scraped the ceiling.) There were boxes and boxes of pizza.

"Good thing our robot was impervious to the ray, Ed," said Knute.

"Yes. There's hardly a robot around that's susceptible to high-fructose corn syrup, which is put into so many packaged foods at the store. It can actually cause diabetes and obesity," Ed said.

The robot spoke in a booming voice, startling everyone:

"It takes human bodies up to three times as long to digest and break down high-fructose corn syrup as it does to digest and break down natural sugar. If you eat enough products containing high-fructose corn syrup, or HFCS, your body is going to struggle to keep up, and may fail. HFCS will mess up many important functions of your fragile, inferior, non-metal bodies, and your blood pressure will skyrocket. You humans would be unhappy in that case," Smash Yucation said flatly.

Ed patted the robot on its foot. "Uh, yeah. Thanks. Anyway, here's what Green Box Foods says about it: If you want to avoid high-fructose corn syrup, eat more organic and all-natural foods or foods that are grown and not processed. Fruits and veggies contain natural sugars that the body can digest easily. Avoid processed foods and you'll avoid the harmful effects of high-fructose corn syrup."

"One thing I don't get," said Xandra. "How did we escape from Obie's bonds? The robot didn't do that."

Malik and Olivia smiled. "That was us," Malik said. "One thing Obie didn't count on was how well mushrooms and olives work together, especially when pizza is involved."

Olivia cut in:

"Mushrooms are a low-calorie food eaten cooked or raw and as garnish to a meal. Dietary mushrooms are a good source of B vitamins, such as riboflavin, niacin, and pantothenic acid, as well as the essential minerals selenium, copper, and potassium. They also lower one's risk of arthritis, cancer, and cardiovascular disease by supporting balanced activities among the white blood cells of the immune system."

"And olives," continued Malik, "contain mostly monounsaturated fat, which lowers blood cholesterol levels, promotes the development of bones and marrow, and helps maintain metabolic balance. They have significant anti-inflammatory properties, delay aging, and assist in the restoration of body tissues, both internal and external."

Olivia was embarrassed, but not too much to add, "We also offer protection against cancer, atherosclerosis, liver disorders and inflammations, and infections."

"Basically," Knute said, "you channeled all the healthy properties you offer onto one spot of the ropes, and we were freed. Right?"

Malik and Olivia exchanged a look.

"Sort of," Olivia said. "What it comes down to is that no one should ever get between me and my pizza." 🌿

THE GREEN BOX LEAGUE OF

NUTRITIOUS JUSTICE

Spell Me

Olivia _ _ _ _ _ _ _

The red phone flashed. Orlando Orange scooped it up.

"Green Box League of Nutritious Justice, Orlando Orange here. Ah, good afternoon, Mr. Mayor. Yes, Mr. Mayor. Certainly, Mr. Mayor. We're on it, sir." Then he hung up the phone and checked his watch. It was four o'clock. Knute Trition, Ed Yucation, and X. R. Cise would be in at five.

Peter Pumpkin, sitting at a nearby activity table and coloring in his coloring book, said, "That the mayor?"

"Yup."

"Crime in progress?"

"Yup."

"What's the caper?"

"It's the Anti-Immune Gang. They're stirring up trouble on Fourth and Cliffside."

"Yeah?"

"That's right."

"Well, let's go. Let's get to work." Peter put his coloring book down and stood as though heading for the door.

"Not so fast, kid. I'm waiting for backup on this one."

"Backup? But we're partners! Let's go, let's do this."

Orlando liked Peter. He didn't want to hurt his feelings — and didn't want to see him get hurt at all.

"Look, kid. We're mismatched, is how I see it. I'm a summer fruit; you're an autumn squash."

"Squash are fruit."

"I'm from all over: Brazil China, India, Mexico, Spain, Egypt, the United States, and Pakistan. You're strictly North American."

"What are you talking about? We're both from the U.S. We live next door to each other."

"I'm raw; you're cooked, boiled, and drained. Get with it."

"What's this all about? Don't you want to be partners?"

"This is the Anti-Immune Gang we're talking about!"

"Yeah?"

"Arteriosclerosis, cancer prevention, cholesterol, constipation, I'd say sure, you're up to that. A guy like me, see, I go up against arthritis; I decrease the risk of lung cancer; I promote healthy vision."

"So? I prevent kidney stones and protect against heart disease and viral infections. I do a good job. What are you driving at?"

"It's like this, kid: you don't boost the immune system! I can't take you on a mission like this. You'll get Jack-o'-lanterned!"

"Huh? Pumpkins are excellent for the immune system!"

This was news to Orlando.

"They are?"

"Absolutely. Pumpkins are packed with powerful antioxidants, particularly beta-carotene, which helps fight off harmful bacteria."

"Really?"

"Well roast my seeds! Yeah, what did you think, we were all about pie and Halloween?"

"Uh ..."

"I'm a superhero, just like you. Come on. We've got work to do. Fourth and Cliffside?"

"Uh, yeah." Orlando was embarrassed.

"Last one there's a rotten egg!" Peter shouted, and with a blur that left Orlando speechless, he blazed a path outside and down the street. By the time Orlando made it to the sidewalk, the blur returned.

Peter was standing there, trailing the whole Anti-Immune Gang, which he'd wrapped in an iron lamppost.

"Partners?" Peter said, extending a hand.

Orlando didn't have a choice. The kid had zest.

"Partners," he agreed. And they shook on it.

156

THE GREEN BOX LEAGUE OF

NUTRITIOUS JUSTICE

Spell Me

Orlando

_____

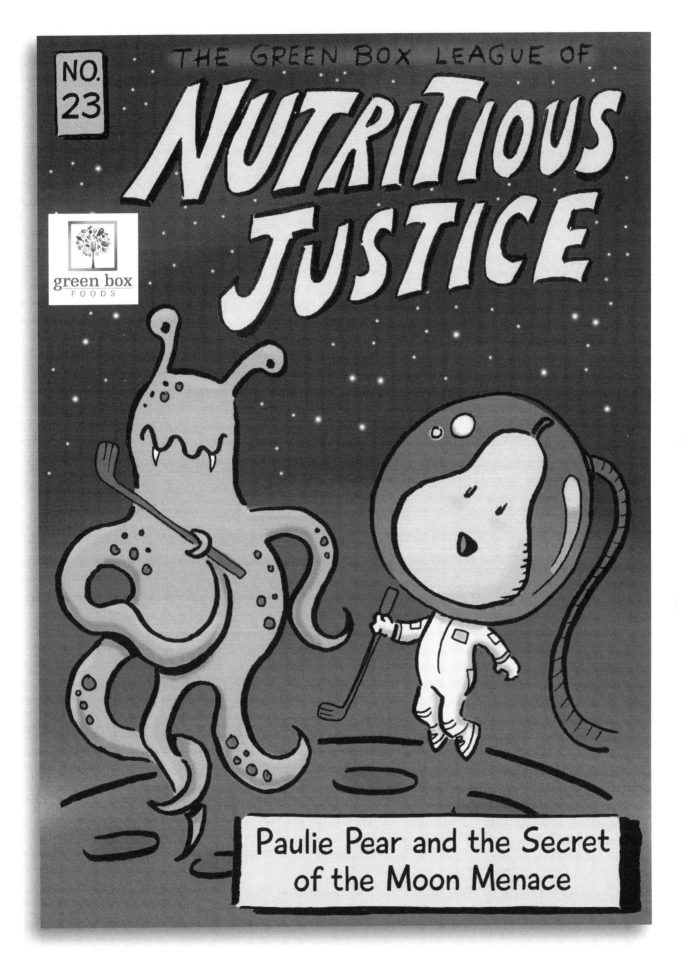

America's first pear test pilot and astronaut, Col. Paulie Pear, was relaxing at home after his celebrated Moon voyage, when the telephone rang. His wife, Pauline, answered from the other room.

"Paulie, it's for you, dear," she said.

"Who is it?"

There was a pause.

"Space monsters."

"What's that?"

"Space monsters. Guy says he met you on the Moon."

"Oh! Space monsters! Yeah. I'll take that."

Paulie leaped up from his chair and ran to take the cordless phone. He kissed his wife on the cheek as she handed him the receiver.

"Jerry, is that you? How've you been? Oh yeah? Oh, you fixed it? That's fantastic. How's your golf game? Uh-huh. You don't say! Well we should hit a few! Yeah! Next time I'm up there!"

Pauline motioned for Paulie's attention.

"Hold on a sec, Jer, my wife wants something."

Pauline whispered, "What's this about monsters? Space monsters?"

"Jer? I'm gonna keep you on hold a second, but first I have to ask: Are you sure the invasion is off? We're all set with that? For now? OK. No, I'm just checking. Yeah. Hold on, Jer."

"Well?" said Pauline.

"This is my friend Jerry. He's a ravenous, hideously tentacled space monster, lives on the Moon. I didn't mention this — I guess maybe it slipped my mind — but there's a whole army of space monsters up there and they were planning to invade. I talked them out of it."

To Jerry, he said: "Still holding? Great. No, I know, I know; this won't take a minute."

Continuing, he told Pauline: "Anyway, what happened was, I landed on the Moon, collected a few rocks, set up a some equipment — you know the routine — and all of a sudden these legions of space monsters showed up and expressed an interest in invading the Earth. They asked if I wouldn't mind giving them directions."

"Directions to the Earth?"

"Yeah! So I figured it's got to be a gag. No one's going to invade the Earth, come on. But it turned out those guys were on the level. They had the ray guns, the rocket ships, the space bazooka: they were all set!"

"You didn't let them!"

"Let them invade? Why, of course not. Rather, I explained that I would appreciate them not invading, and pointed out that, in fact, as a superhero with the Green Box League of Nutritious Justice I couldn't let them invade. I simply wasn't allowed to."

"What happened next?"

"Well, they wanted proof that I was a superhero, naturally, so I explained that I'm an excellent source of dietary fiber and a good source of vitamin C, a proven antioxidant; that I contain no saturated fat, sodium, or cholesterol; and that I reduce inflammation and prevent heart disease, type 2 diabetes, and even cancer.

"So you convinced them?"

"Not with that alone. I also had to explain about red pears being different from green pears, how Anjous are refreshingly sweet and juicy with a hint of citrus; how red Anjous are aromatic, juicy, and fresh; that Bartletts bring a signature pear flavor with abundant juice … Everything. I told them about Boscs with their crisp and woodsy taste and honey sweetness, and everything I could remember about the varieties Comice, Concorde, Forelle, Seckel, and Starkrimson, all of which abound with nutrients."

"And that impressed them?"

"You know, it did, but to drive my point home I walked over and tied their space bazooka into a pretzel knot. After that we got along great, and got in some Moon golf, like I said. Nice guys,

the space monsters. This guy calling me is Jerry, their leader."

That reminded Paulie that Jerry was still on the line.

"Hello, Jerry? Jer? Are you there? Hello? Hello?"

"Was he there?"

Paulie shrugged, and handed Pauline the phone. "He hung up. I'm sure if it was important we'll hear from him again."

THE GREEN BOX LEAGUE OF

NUTRITIOUS JUSTICE

Spell Me

Paulie _ _ _ _ _

t just so happened that Lydia Lima Bean, Evie Edamame, Gertie Green Bean, and Prudence Pea each earned their Presidential Active Lifestyle Award (PALA+) on the very same day, so it was a very exciting — and happy — day at the Green Box League of Nutritious Justice.

Xandra "X. R." Cise helped the young heroes hang their certificates up for all to see.

"I am superproud of all of you. You were all active for at least sixty minutes a day, at least five days a week, for six out of eight weeks, and you stuck with your healthy eating goals. You all deserve this," she said.

Prudence Pea, who loved to walk and skip and hike and snowshoe, was smiling from ear to ear.

"I used a pedometer to count off my paces and physical intensity, and put in 11,000 to 13,000 whole steps a day to earn my award!" she said.

Then all the friends eagerly talked about their food choices over the past six weeks:

"I made half my plate fruits and vegetables!"

"I made half the grains I ate whole grains!"

"I chose all-natural and organic dairy!"

"I drank water instead of sugary drinks!"

Then Xandra asked for a show of hands:

"Who here chose lean sources of protein?"

All hands went up.

"Who here compared sodium in foods like soup and frozen meals and choose foods with less sodium?"

All hands went up.

"Who made sure to eat some treats our friend Samantha Seafood showed us?"

Each of the kids loved trying new foods from the sea.

"And I paid extra attention to portion size," Lydia said proudly.

The wall where the heroes hung up their award certificates was getting crowded. Gold and silver trophies were filling up the display case. It was so exciting for Xandra to help the kids in her care find new ways to show themselves and others what they could do.

LATER THAT WEEK, the heroes added a new award to the wall: the key to the city, a gift from the mayor, for helping save so many citizens from having their blood sugar levels rise too quickly.

The proclamation read, in part, "Whereas Lydia Lima Bean, Evie Edamame, Gertie Green Bean, and Prudence Pea, being members in good standing in the Green Box League of Nutritious Justice, and of remarkably high fiber of character, and being true heroes to us all, have saved us once again from the Legion of Unhealthy Injustice, we thank them and hold them up to all as pillars of our community."

And the oversized brass key was lovely.

But for Lydia, Evie, Gertie, and Prudence, that PALA+ award, which came all the way from Green Box Foods itself, was the most special.

"Why is that?" Xandra asked.

"Because whatever else we might do for the city or the world, earning that PALA+ award was something we earned for ourselves," Prudence Pea said.

Then all the kids ran outside to play. 🌿

THE GREEN BOX LEAGUE OF

NUTRITIOUS JUSTICE

Spell Me

Lydia _ _ _ _ _ _ _ _

"Band practice, soccer practice, superhero training, and tons of homework, plus all my chores at home. When am I supposed to find time to write and direct a skit for the school talent show?"

This was Knute Trition at the family's kitchen table, complaining to his dad, who set his newspaper aside and listened patiently. He'd been a kid once too, and remembered how sometimes it just seemed that life was so unfair, that the stakes were always so high. Why, if he could do it all over again …

"Son, if there's one thing I know about you, that your mother and I are so proud of, it's that you don't give up. You stick with it, whatever it is, and inspire other people to do their best too. I know you can write an excellent skit, and you'll fit in all your obligations and do a great job. What's really going on?"

Knute was so happy his father had returned from the hospital last year with such courage and determination. He was almost a new man. Since his discharge, Tom had worked really hard to lose all his excess weight and keep it off, and he was once again a figure of calm and strength for the family. His health meant the family was happy and whole.

"Maybe that's it, Dad. Maybe I've just been going it alone on this skit. Maybe I should ask for help: bring in the team to lend a hand."

"Sounds smart to me, Knute. I think you're on the right track," Tom Trition said with a smile. "Let me know what I can do to pitch in. And don't forget about our hike this evening before supper."

Eavesdropping at the window was Salty Snake, whose tail now twitched with interest.

AT THE SCHOOL, Knute had gathered some friends: Bobby Bean, Cornelius Corn, Logan Lime, Octavio Onion, and Pasquale Peppers. They were on the wide, empty stage of the auditorium.

"I have an idea for a skit," Knute said. "But I need your help. What do you think we can add to it to make it better?"

"What's the idea, Knute?" This was little Bobby Bean, who thought Knute was the greatest guy in the world.

"We'll play ourselves. Bobby, you're an excellent source of fiber and vegetarian protein, right?"

"You bet, Knute! I'm good for you and way filling. Why?"

"Hold that thought. Now, you, Octavio: you lower blood levels of cholesterol and triglycerides, and improve cell membrane function in red blood cells. Plus you have really strong natural antibacterial properties, and prevent or treat many common diseases, including various kinds of cancer, coronary heart disease, type 2 diabetes, and cataracts."

"If I'm lyin' I'm cryin," Octavio said, then struck a relaxed but eager judo pose to show how prepared he was for whatever Knute might throw at him.

Knute smiled. He liked Octavio's enthusiasm.

"Where's Pasquale? Ah, there you are. Pasquale, you know all about the five main species of peppers, from sweet to spicy. Can you do a good jalapeño?"

Pasquale thought for a moment.

"Sure, Knute. Even though there are a lot of types of peppers, we all protect the cardiovascular system, pitch in on blood sugar regulation, and

are rich in vitamins A and C."

"You also boost the immune system, right?"

"Absolutely! What's this skit about? I'm dying to know!"

"I'll get there, I promise. First: how hot can you get?"

"As hot as you need. Hot peppers contain the chemical capsaicin, which in strong enough concentrations is like the hottest sauce there is. I like being mild most of the time, though," Pasquale said.

"OK, that's perfect. Cornelius, you're up. I know you can act; you're always at the theater. You're strong on phytonutrients, or plant-based nutrients, am I correct?"

"Sure, Knute. Vitamin C, manganese … Anything you need," Cornelius said. Whatever he said was usually sure and to the point, a habit he picked up from his father, who was a colonel.

Knute stopped. He'd thought he'd heard a hiss from the seats in the audience, but they were empty.

He continued:

"Last but not least we have Logan Lime. Hi, Logan!"

Logan was shy, but he loved Knute too. He waved.

"Can you act, Logan?"

Logan nodded, with a smile.

"OK. Logan, I know your family pretty well. You as a lime are smaller and less sour than lemons, which is perfect for this. You're also a perfect all-natural dietary addition for anyone working to prevent cancer or support cancer remission and treatment."

"I'm zesty!" Logan said.

"Yes, you are. OK, I think we have most of what we need for ... dun dun *dunnn* ... a salsa!"

Everyone looked around and smiled at each other. They saw how this could work.

"But we need tomatoes, Knute! What about tomatoes?" said Logan.

Logan was right. A proper salsa should have tomatoes.

"I'll be right back!" Knute said, and hopped offstage. He left the room and ran off out of view. A few moments later he returned leading a very confused Tom Tomato, the science teacher.

"Hop right on up, Mr. Tomato, and I'll explain," Knute said.

Tom was in excellent shape, and needed no help joining the young actors.

Mr. Tomato, we were just planning to make a salsa for the school talent show skit. You'd be perfect in it, because you lower total cholesterol levels, triglyceride levels, and LDL cholesterol in the bloodstream."

"I'm flattered, Knute. I do protect the cardiovascular system — specifically the arteries — from clogging, and I go with anything. Why, I'll even go along with this unusual adventure!" he said merrily.

And then there was that soft, rattling hiss from somewhere nearby the empty chairs. It worried Knute.

For the rest of the day he and the actors wrote lines and rehearsed, getting their timing just right — but when all was said and done, something was missing.

"I just can't put my finger on it. We have tomato, onion, lime, bell pepper, corn, and even cilantro."

Cilantro, a foreign exchange student, smiled and dipped her green leaves sweetly.

"But something's missing. Let's see. We all come together, mix it up, and then serve on baked chicken, fish, or pork: they said they could help. But what's the missing ingredient?" Knute wondered.

"It's me! Salt!"

All eyes on the stage looked down to where the audience would sit. There, undulating on the cool tile, was Salty Snake, one of Knute Trition and the Green Box League of Nutritious Justice's worst enemies. He was hissing, and the saltshaker at the tip of his tail rattled.

"You need sssalt for salsa! You need me to save you for a change, Knute Trition!" Salty said.

All the others on the stage seemed to want to rush to capture the foe, but Knute held them back. "Go on," he said.

Salty coiled and uncoiled as he spoke. He was uncomfortable being in the spotlight. But what he had to say was important:

"Sssalt has been the best-known food preservative, especially for meat, for many thousands of years. You need dietary sodium to live, so that your cells function."

"You're dangerous," Knute said. "Excessive salt—"

"—That'sss just it!" the snake interrupted. "Excessive sssalt leads to hypertension and heart disease. Not just the right amount! And for people who shouldn't have salt, there are optionsss!"

Knute nodded. "AlsoSalt and Original Himalayan Crystal Salt."

"That'sss right. But in a little thing like salsa? One dish? I'd like ..."

"What?" asked Knute.

"I'd like to be in the ssskit. I'm not all bad," Salty hissed. If snakes could weep, a single, salty tear might have welled up.

Knute thought about it. "What do you say, guys? A little salt in the salsa? In moderation? It would really help us out."

Mr. Tomato blanched. "I just want to say, Knute, that the reason Salty Snake here is a villain is that far too many people put far too much salt in too much of their food. And this slithery scoundrel sneaks an overabundance of it into processed foods even without most consumers knowing about it. The health costs are enormous."

"Yesss," agreed Salty. "But just a little bit for sssalsa. I just want to act," he said.

The actors talked it over.

A WEEK LATER the curtain rose on the best skit of the show. The program read:

"Salsa, rice, and beans"

Serve this colorful salsa with grilled or baked chicken, fish, or pork.

Ingredients:

2 cups frozen corn kernels, thawed

⅓ cup chopped purple onion

¼ cup chopped red bell pepper

3 tablespoons chopped fresh cilantro

2 tablespoons fresh lime juice

1 to 2 tablespoons finely chopped jalapeño pepper

½ teaspoon salt

Preparation:

Combine all ingredients in a small bowl. Cover and refrigerate for 2 to 4 hours. Remove from refrigerator about 30 minutes before serving. Serve corn salsa with grilled meat or poultry.

Makes about 3 cups corn salsa.

THAT NIGHT Knute, Bobby Bean, Octavio Onion, Tom Tomato, Pasquale Peppers, Logan Lime, Cilantro, and Cornelius Corn went out to dinner to celebrate, with Knute's parents footing the bill. They'd have some ice cream later. Nobody could remember the last time they had so much fun together.

"The show was a smash hit! You were all fantastic! Thank you for giving it your all," Knute said.

"I knew you could do it, son," Tom said with a happy heart.

And then, holding the group's trophy for best performance at the talent show, Bobby summed it up for everyone:

"All for one and one for all, Knute: whether fighting O.BC.D. or entertaining a crowd, the Green Box League of Nutritious Justice — and now salsa — saves the day!"

As for Salty Snake, proud of himself for having done some good, however temporary, slipped away from the group unnoticed. He slithered toward home to plot his next ssscheme.

THE GREEN BOX LEAGUE OF NUTRITIOUS JUSTICE

Spell Me

Tom _ _ _ _ _ _ _

Reports were coming in from all over the world: nobody was sleeping. Lights were kept on too late; televisions and computers were playing at all hours; folks were staring into the glowing rectangles of their mobile devices in bed. And they were waking up cranky, and not feeling rested or recharged.

"Knute, it's a health crisis," the President complained. "Somehow or other everyone's suffering from lack of sleep. They're eating too much before bed, particularly sugary foods and drinks. Without enough sleep, at least eight hours, their bodies can't recover from the day."

"I know, Mr. President. Green Box Foods put out the alert some time ago. Sleep is critical to health and wellness. A lack of sleep, as we see today, leads youth to being overweight and obese, which leads to greater risk diseases such as cardiovascular disease, diabetes, and cancer. In fact, overweight children now suffer from what we previously considered to be adult diseases: type 2 diabetes, liver and kidney disease, sleep apnea, high blood pressure, liver disease, high cholesterol, and joint pain."

"What can we do, Knute?"

"Mr. President, we know 80 percent of all chronic diseases can be prevented by lifestyle change, including proper nutrition and exercise. And backing all that is a good night's sleep. So we have to ask ourselves, Who would want to take a good night's sleep out of the picture?"

"You don't mean ..."

"I do. It's O.BC.D. Somehow he's back in action. Don't worry, Mr. President. I'll find him. I'll finish him for good this time, and then Sammy Sleep, the great, unsung hero of the League of Nutritious Justice, will be back on the job, and we'll all be able to relax."

Knute left the Oval Office and the White House, and then, with a confident leap and a bound, streaked so fast for the wide-open sky that he trailed a sonic boom.

IT WAS A VERY surprised O.BC.D. indeed who saw Knute Trition standing in the villain's lair, directly under a hole in the roof. Bits of plaster and sawdust sifted around him. Knute was more serious than Obie had ever seen him.

"What's the meaning of this intrusion? I've a mind to call the police!"

"Go ahead, Obie. In fact, I'll save you the trouble. I'll take you there myself. But first tell me one thing: How are you stopping people from getting enough sleep? What's your scheme?"

Obie looked around nervously. His gaze fell on a door marked Authorized Bad Guys Only. He'd given away the location to his lab entrance.

"Show me," Knute said, and led Obie toward the door.

Inside, Obie turned on the light. And there was Sammy Sleep in a glass chamber. Obie had used a ray to siphon all the parts of Sammy Sleep from bedrooms all over the world.

"How do I reverse this? How do we open this?" Knute demanded.

Obie knew Knute wasn't kidding around. He pushed a green button on his control panel, and the glass chamber spun open. Sammy was free.

"Knute, I knew you'd come," Sammy said. "I'm sorry I let this menace capture me."

"Sammy, I'm just glad you're safe. But the

people need you. Do what you have to do, and I'll see you soon."

With that, Sammy turned into a collection of soft lights and shadows, and flew away on his most important mission yet: to restore the balance of what Obie had upset in billions of homes ...

"As for you," Knute began ...

Obie fell to his nubby little knees.

"Please, Knute. I know I don't deserve any sympathy after all I've done. I know I'm responsible for countless hospital visits, missed opportunities, and trillions of dollars in suffering and lost productivity. Believe me, I know I've made awful, selfish, terrible mistakes with people's lives. But ..."

"But?"

"But I'm just so tired. I haven't had a wink of sleep all week. I can't think clearly to save my life right now. Let me take a nap. That's all I ask."

Knute was tired too. But he hadn't lost his sense of justice.

"You'll get all the sleep you want, Obie. Or as much as the warden will allow." And with that he hauled him off to the police station, to file his complaint.

ON THE NEWS that night the President made sure to thank Knute and the Green Box League of Nutritious Justice not only for rescuing Sammy Sleep, but also for all the work they had started in the realm of nutrition, exercise, and education, and for inspiring millions of kids, and millions of families, to be the best they could be.

Knute watched with satisfaction as the President thanked Ed Yucation and Xandra Risa "X. R." Cise for excellence in promoting the Presidential Youth Fitness Program, which Green Box Foods supports through the Presidential Active Lifestyle Award (PALA+) challenge.

And the President, joined now by his wife, called on mothers and fathers, teachers, aunts, uncles, grandparents, employers, and institutions to continue to do all they could to promote healthy living in America's youth.

"The decisions you make about what foods to buy, how you feed your family, your workers, your friends, this all is a lesson our kids are studying. You can teach them well, living healthfully by example, and building choice by choice a strong America and a proud future. I know we can. And I know you will."

Now all the heroes had joined Knute to watch the speech. Adam Apple, Cosmo Cucumber, Tabitha Turkey, Wally Watermelon. The room filled with dozens of heroes eager to see the President speak so passionately about the power of personal responsibility in health, fitness, and nutrition. Nothing else was more important.

"My family, like yours, is busy. Every day there are a million things demanding our attention. It's no less true for you than it is for me. Before I am the President, I am a father. Before I am the Commander in Chief, I am an American. The risks we face on the world stage are insurmountable unless we first win the war at home. The war with the forces which would see us fail before we even get out of bed."

Ed and Xandra stood with Knute. They had begun this together.

"Do you get enough uninterrupted, quality sleep, free from distraction and late-night snacks?

Do you drink enough water? Do you spend enough time exercising, and are you tracking your progress and taking on increasing challenges? Do you eat an abundance of fruits and vegetables, and lean, all-natural organic meat? Or if not meat, then a healthful blend of plant-based proteins?"

Everyone in the room whispered yes, yes, of course. We are superheroes.

"And are you looking for ways to lead by example? Is your kitchen well stocked with whole foods, nothing packaged, and nothing laced with strange chemicals, excess sodium, refined sugar, and high-fructose corn syrup? Can you run and jump and swim and hike? Can you make America stronger by making yourself a little bit stronger? And can you say with confidence that obesity is your fight, and you will not back down, you will not yield to advertised temptation, and you will not give yourself to this monster, this killer?"

The President looked steadily into the camera.

"For make no mistake: obesity is a killer. And it is a killer so many of its victims choose. They invite it into their homes and places of work, their places of worship. And if we can choose it in, we can certainly choose it out. We can stand up to obesity and its cohorts, the other creatures and

176

killers it creates, and we can say, 'No more. This is not the life I want for myself. These are not the expenses I want my children, grandchildren, and nation to bear.'"

Now the President smiled.

"I was reminded today of what true courage is, what strength there is in simple conviction and a clear vision. Today I met with Knute Trition of the Green Box League of Nutritious Justice, right here in the Oval Office, and he told me something that resonates still, and I expect always will. Knute said to me, 'Mr. President, we can do this. We'll take the fight to obesity. And we won't be alone. Whoever you are, wherever you're starting from, it's never too late to change for the best.'"

Listening, and surrounded by his friends, Knute felt love all-around him, as he did at home, with his parents and brother near.

The President was wrapping up his remarks.

"I choose health and wellness for myself and my family. And I wish it for you and yours. And you don't need the government to give it to you. You have the power, and the responsibility, and with the Green Box League of Nutritious Justice, the tools, to provide it for yourselves. I know we can do great things. I know we are a great people. Let's take care of ourselves, and everything else will fall into place. Have a good night. Sleep well. Thank you, and God bless America."

AT THE END of that day's battles, after a nice supper, a relaxing walk, and time to chat, digest, and reflect, sleep did come to the Green Box League of Nutritious Justice.

As the Moon rose over League headquarters, a good night's sleep came to all the fruits and vegetables, snug in their beds.

Restful sleep came to the all-natural lean meats, tired from a full day's work.

Recuperative sleep came to everyone who needed cells repaired, fluids balanced, and bodies detoxified.

Sleep came to the heroes who had flown, or run, or leaped, or written, or splashed. Sleep came to the young and the old. Everyone was comfortable.

X. R. Cise smiled and said good night to her little friends. She went to sleep.

Ed Yucation, who had ideas for a bigger, faster, better robot, slept so his mind could work out the details, or maybe dream of fields and flowers.

Across the world all the heroes settled down, and all the villains too, and water grew calm. Stars sparkled. The world was repairing itself and growing stronger, and this important work would take many hours.

Knute Trition, too, after setting all the outside alarms, making sure he had his bag packed for school the next day, and saying a few silent words of thanks for all that he had, and for all he was being allowed to do for so many people, settled in to his bed, got perfectly comfortable, and fell asleep.

Sammy Sleep, the great, unsung hero of the League of Nutritious Justice, stood watch over all, and smiled. It had been a great day.

Tomorrow, he knew, would be even better.

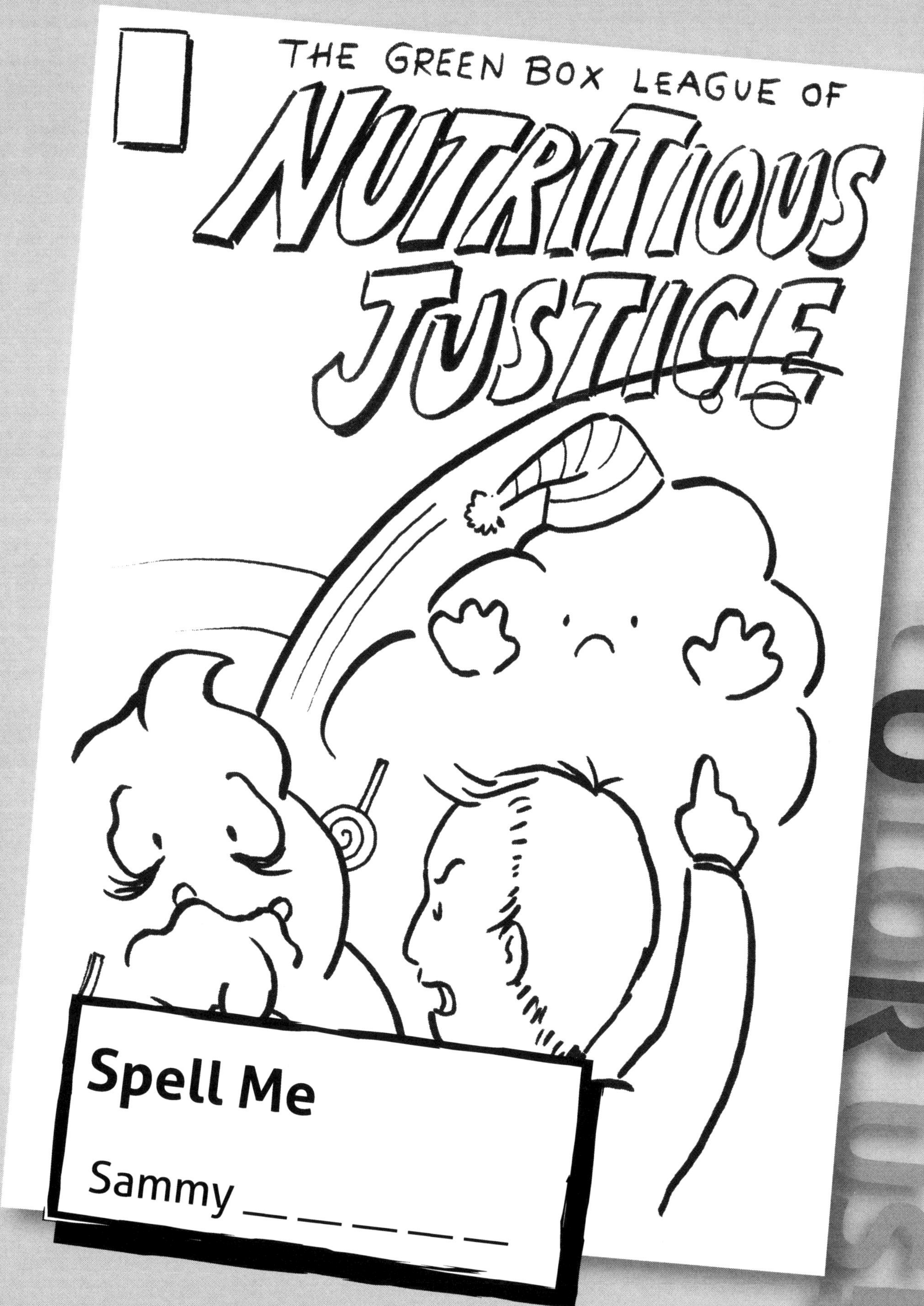

Spell Me

Sammy _ _ _ _ _ _

COLOUR US!

How Your Family Can Eat Healthfully

utrition, exercise, and education are the keys to living a good long life. Here we pull out all the stops on education, showing you what Dr. Keith Kantor and registered dietitian and personal trainer Dana Yarn mean when they say living well is up to each of us. Whether making mealtime a family time, setting a good example for children, or beating back kitchen accidents, diabetes, heart disease, hypertension, and obesity, these reports have you covered.

Quick Reference

HEALTH

The Difference Between USDA and ANFCNA All-Natural and USDA Organic

DR. KEITH KANTOR, N.D., PH.D.

CONSUMERS ARE FLOCKING TO PRODUCTS MARKED "all-natural" or "organic" in greater numbers every year. Such products include natural and organic foods, dietary supplements, pet foods, health and beauty products, and "green" cleaning supplies: those that get the job done with the least burden passed on to our finely tuned bodily and environmental systems.

Generally, all-natural products, as advertised so by the All-Natural Food Council of North America (ANFCNA), are considered those formulated without artificial ingredients and that are minimally processed. In comparison, the United States Department of Agriculture's (USDA's) National Organic Program regulates standards for any farm, wild crop harvesting, or handling operation that wants to sell an agricultural product as organically produced.

I'm delighted to help you understand what's behind each of these important labeling programs so that you'll know what you're buying and what it means to consume the food that's farmed, processed, and packaged for your family.

The main difference between both USDA Organic and USDA All-Natural is in their areas of concentration. Organic focuses on *production*, how food is farmed:

— No synthetic (non-biological) fertilizer can be used in the growing of crops.

— No synthetic pest management can be used on the crops.

— The soil is tested to make sure non-biologics had not been used for five to seven years.

— Organic livestock can be fed only from crops meeting the above criteria.

— Ranchers are not allowed to give the animals they're raising synthetic antibiotics or hormones.

This is where production stops, and where organic labeling stops. Once the crop or animal is raised under

these criteria, and handed off to production facilities, they move beyond the purview of the USDA National Organic Program.

The USDA All-Natural and ANFCNA programs go further, covering food *processing* as well, and so are incredibly important.

First, let's examine the farming aspect of USDA All-Natural.

— Similar to organic, no synthetic fertilizer can be used during the growing cycle.

— No non-biological pest management can be used during the growing cycle of the crops, or the raising of the animal.

USDA All-Natural and USDA Organic differ in their attention to the growing cycle: all-natural concerns itself with the current growing cycle; organic covers the past five to seven years.

In other words, with USDA all-natural crops, trace amounts of synthetic fertilizer or non-biological herbicides might linger in the soil. Fortunately, these traces are miniscule — measured in nanograms (millionths of a gram) — and at these quantities have not been shown to harm humans.

All-natural livestock can also be fed from crops that have these few nanograms of residue in the soil. Once the crop is grown, or the animal is raised and given to the production facility, the strict guidelines of USDA and ANFCNA All-Natural kick in.

For example, machinery coming into contact with the product must be steam-, not bleach-cleaned, as USDA Organic labeling permits.

Then there's packaging: USDA Organic permits packaging in Styrofoam trays and cellophane wrap, and non-natural papers in separating foodstuffs. That's not so under USDA and ANFCNA All-Natural certification, where only natural products such as rice paper are permitted to come into contact with food.

Another major difference is in freezing: where USDA Organic allows freezing using conventional methods that allow crystallization — slow freezing, below 32 degrees Fahrenheit — USDA and ANFCNA All-Natural rules permit only blast freezing, a process that takes the item down to minus 50 degrees Fahrenheit in less than a heartbeat.

This is important because only blast freezing prevents crystallization that otherwise would support anaerobic bacteria, or bacteria that don't need oxygen to live, such as *E. coli.*

Further, USDA and ANFCNA guidelines insist food products be vacuum-sealed, which removes the oxygen aerobic bacteria, such as salmonella, need to live. The process provides for incredible food safety and quality.

So as you can see, both USDA Organic and USDA and ANFCNA All-Natural programs have their merits. In my opinion, the benefits to the consumer in cleaning processing machinery with steam rather than bleach, and eliminating both anaerobic and aerobic bacteria, easily mitigate the fact of a few inconsequential nanograms of synthetic fertilizer left lingering in the soil.

I've given you these facts about USDA Organic and USDA and ANFCNA All-Natural for your use in making an informed decision about healthy living and consumer protection.

I know what I look for in a label assuring me of the best for my family. Now you can choose what's best for yourself and yours.

Allergies and Nutrition

DANA YARN, R.D., L.D., AND DR. KEITH KANTOR, N.D., PH.D.

WHAT WE EAT AFFECTS EVERYTHING ABOUT us, from our complexion to our mood to our heart health — and how we feel affects our productivity and everyone around us, whether it's friends, family, or co-workers.

Allergies are a hypersensitive reaction to a particular stimulus, which in this case we call an allergen. We know about hay fever, of course, which makes many people sneeze, and our eyes water; some people are allergic to dust mites, which make us itch and develop rashes.

But there are also food allergies, which are abnormal immune system responses to specific foods. These episodes can be uncomfortable, debilitating, sometimes severe, and — when untreated — sometimes fatal. Fortunately, as with most afflictions, diet is the key to living better.

Here's what you need to know to keep yourself and your family breathing easy and enjoying as varied and full a diet as possible, for a happy, active life.

Allergies vs. intolerance

According to the Mayo Clinic, food allergy affects an estimated 6 to 8 percent of children younger than age 5 and about 3 to 4 percent of adults. "While there's no cure," the Mayo Clinic notes, "some children outgrow their food allergy as they get older. It's easy to confuse a food allergy with a much more common reaction known as food intolerance. While bothersome, food intolerance is a less serious condition that does not involve the immune system."

Common symptoms include:

— Tingling or itching in the mouth

— Hives, itching, or eczema

— Swelling of the lips, face, tongue, and throat, or other parts of the body

— Wheezing, nasal congestion, or trouble breathing

— Abdominal pain, diarrhea, nausea or vomiting

— Dizziness, lightheadedness, or fainting

182

Anaphylaxis

In some people, a food allergy can trigger a severe allergic reaction called anaphylaxis. This can cause life-threatening symptoms, including:

— Constriction and tightening of airways

— A swollen throat or the sensation of a lump in your throat that makes breathing difficult

— Shock, with a severe drop in blood pressure

— Rapid pulse

— Dizziness, lightheadedness, or loss of consciousness

Emergency treatment is critical for anaphylaxis. Untreated, anaphylaxis can cause a coma or death.

Food allergy at a glance

• Food allergies are not common, but can be serious.

• Food allergies differ from food intolerance, which is far more common.

• Food allergies common in adults are not the same as those that typically afflict children.

• Children can outgrow their food allergies, but adults usually do not.

• A food allergy diagnosis is made with a detailed history, the patient's diet diary, or an elimination diet.

• Food allergy is treated primarily by dietary avoidance.

Diagnosis

The doctor makes this assessment with the help of a detailed history from the patient or the patient's caregivers. He or she then confirms the diagnosis by the more objective skin tests, blood tests, or food challenges.

Treatment

• Dietary avoidance: Avoiding the offending dietary allergen is the primary treatment for a food allergy. Once a food to which the patient is sensitive has been identified, that food must be removed from the diet. To do this, affected people need to be extra alert to the ingredients in the foods they're buying at the market or ordering off the restaurant menu.

• Treating an anaphylactic reaction: People with severe food allergies must be prepared to treat an anaphylactic reaction. Even those who know a lot about their own allergies can either make an error or be served food that does not comply with their instructions.

To protect themselves, people who have had anaphylactic reactions to a food should wear medical alert bracelets or necklaces stating that they have a food allergy and that they are subject to severe reactions. These individuals should also always carry a syringe of adrenaline, obtained by prescription from their doctor, and be prepared to self-administer if they think they are developing an allergic reaction.

Most common food allergies

Any food has the potential to trigger a food allergy, given that everyone's immune systems are unique. But as it happens, a mere handful of foods are implicated in 90 percent of allergic reactions to food, and we know them as The Big Eight:

• Milk

• Eggs

• Peanuts (ground nuts)

• Nuts from trees (including Brazil nuts, hazelnuts, almonds, and walnuts)

• Fish

• Shellfish (including mussels, crab, and shrimp)

• Soy

• Wheat

In children, most allergic reactions to food are to milk, peanuts, nuts from trees, eggs, soy, and wheat.

Most children grow out of most allergic reactions to food in early childhood.

In adults, most allergic reactions are to peanuts, nuts, fish, shellfish, citrus fruit, and wheat.

All-natural, chemically pure foods put those who suffer from allergies at less risk than from processed foods, which may have been cross-contaminated or contain undisclosed ingredients. Look for healthy food options that won't trigger your allergies.

Supplementation

When we cut out foods we're allergic to, we're also cutting out the entire nutritional benefit those foods would bring. It's more important than ever, in that case, to bring in food supplements to protect against dietary deficiencies. Check the label for the NPA seal of all-natural manufacturing practices, and know that your doctor may recommend additional supplements:

— Omega-3 fatty acids from krill or fish oil
— Multivitamin

References

LaValle J.B., Yale S.L. Cracking the Metabolic Code®. Laguna Beach: Basic Health Publications, Inc; 2004; pgs 189-203.

Montalto M., et al. Adverse reactions to food: allergies and intolerances. Dig Dis. 2008; 26 (2): 96-103

Murry, Michael T., and Pizzorno, Joseph, The Encyclopedia of Natural Medicine 3rd Edition.

Asthma and Nutrition

DANA YARN, R.D., L.D., AND DR. KEITH KANTOR, N.D., PH.D.

WHAT YOU EAT CAN help you breathe? Absolutely.

No doubt we've all seen children and adults managing small inhalers to help them breathe, and thought, "She has asthma." But what is asthma? Is there anything we can do to help a loved one with this affliction? And if we, or someone we care for, have been diagnosed with asthma or other respiratory disease, how can a good diet help?

Here's the background: asthma is a chronic disease of the airways that makes breathing difficult for an estimated 22 million Americans. Characterized by an inflammation of the air passages, it results in a temporary narrowing of the airways that carry oxygen to the lungs.

Symptoms include coughing, wheezing, shortness of breath, and chest tightness, especially early in the morning and at night. (Incidentally, that inhaler you've seen, if you're not familiar with it, is a metered-dose inhaler, a device that delivers a specific amount of medication to the lungs.)

The incidence of asthma has risen in the United States during the past three decades, and many researchers believe that our changing diets have something to do with this. As Americans eat fewer and fewer fruits and vegetables, and more processed foods, could it be that we're bumping up our risk of developing asthma? One recent study of asthma and diet showed that teens with poor nutrition were more likely to develop asthma symptoms.

Studies show that those who didn't get enough fruits and other foods with vitamins C and E and omega-3 fatty acids were the most likely to suffer poor lung function. Moreover, the overweight and obese suffer more severe asthma.

Even with that — and with asthma in children on the rise — with proper treatment for symptoms, kids and adults can live a normal, happy, active lifestyle. Make a good diet, a healthful diet, an integral part of your overall asthma treatment plan.

Natural and nutritional remedies

First, let's take a look at natural and nutritional remedies for asthma. In contrast to pharmaceuticals, natural remedies may help to control asthma symptoms gently and inexpensively: natural relaxation therapy, such as deep abdominal breathing, muscle relaxation, and yoga, can help relieve stress when an asthma attack is brought on by emotional stress.

It's thought that omega-3 fatty acids, found naturally in heart-healthy, high-fat fish such as salmon, mackerel, and cod, allow the body to naturally decrease inflammation. In addition to its wealth of omega-3s, salmon provides protein, calcium, magnesium, some carotenoids, and B vitamins. (Vitamin B-6 helps to boost the immune system, which prevents diseases and flare-ups.)

These antioxidants are found in quality seafood, and can help the body prevent cell damage.

Now, what can we do to help ward off asthma attacks? Many people with asthma feel short of breath when their stomachs are full, as the diaphragm doesn't work to its full efficiency. Satisfy your nutritional needs, keep your stomach comfortable, and help your diaphragm to work better by eating smaller, more frequent meals. Smaller meals also reduce the chance of reflux, which can also trigger an asthma attack.

Helpful tips:
— Don't hold your breath while you chew.
— Stop eating if you need to catch your breath.
— Relax and sit down at mealtime.
— Batch cook: Double or triple your favorite recipes and keep leftovers in your freezer for when you don't feel like cooking. This way, when you're short on time, you'll avoid fast foods that are processed and full of chemicals, which can irritate asthma. (And you'll reduce your stress around shopping, cooking, and cleaning.)

Managing asthma

There's no cure for asthma, but you can manage it through lifestyle factors:
— Keep an asthma diary to track your symptoms and medication use.
— Avoid asthma triggers or causes of asthma, including outdoor irritants such as smog, and dietary sources of inflammation such as dairy, peanuts, soy, and gluten.

— Seek medical advice and treatment for coexisting problems that can worsen asthma symptoms, such as GERD, allergic rhinitis, and sinusitis.
— Exercise daily to maximize your aerobic fitness.
— Prevent exercise-induced asthma by medicating before exercise.
— Eat all-natural, nutritious foods to maximize your immune defenses against viral and bacterial infections.
— Maintain a normal weight.
— Get plenty of restful sleep.

Supplementation

In order to keep asthma flare-ups to a minimum, supplement your healthy diet of lean protein, fruits, vegetables, whole grains, and heart-healthy fats with immune-system-boosting supplements.

These supplements have been shown to decrease asthma flare-ups. Check the label for the NPA seal of all-natural manufacturing practices, and know that your doctor may recommend additional supplements:
— Omega-3 fatty acids from fish or krill oil
— Multivitamin
— Vitamins C and E
— Super greens and/or resveratrol, a pure form of antioxidants to ensure that the body is in a state of balance and boost immunity.
— Probiotics, which can build up the gut flora and make athsma attacks less severe.

References

Woolcock, A. J., Peat, J. K. (1997) Evidence for the increase in asthma worldwide. Ciba Found Symp 206: 122–134.

Birch, L. L., Marlin, D. W., Rotter, J. (1984) Eating as the "means" activity in a contingency: effects on young children's food preference. Child Dev 55: 431–439.

Ratio of Omega 6 to Omega-3 Fatty Acids and Childhood Asthma. 2004, Vol. 41, No. 3, pages 319-326

Prevent and Maintain Diabetes Through Diet

DR. KEITH KANTOR, N.D., PH.D.

I F BY EATING WELL FROM A RICH VARIETY OF GOOD FOODS and getting plenty of exercise you could control or prevent disease, would you? What we eat can either help us live long, happy lives or set the stage for costly disease and early death. What we eat is up to us, along with the results.

Take diabetes mellitus, or simply diabetes, a usually lifelong (chronic) disease in which the body can't control the amount of fuel in the blood. Just as we fuel cars with gasoline, we power our body's cells with glucose, which the body converts from sugar, starches, and other food and delivers to our cells, our body's trillions of little engines.

But sometimes things go wrong involving insulin, and then the blood sugar level gets out of whack. The cells don't get enough fuel, and the free blood sugar can lead to complications such as kidney damage, neurological damage, cardiovascular damage, damage to the retina, and damage to the feet and legs.

As the American Diabetes Association describes, there are three type of diabetes:

Type 1 diabetes is usually diagnosed in children and young adults, and was previously known as juvenile diabetes. In type 1 diabetes, the body does not produce insulin. If you have type 1 diabetes, you'll need injections of insulin to make sure you don't get hyperglycaemia — too much blood sugar.

If you have **type 2 diabetes** your body can't use insulin properly. This is called insulin resistance. At first, your pancreas makes extra insulin to make up for it, but over time it isn't able to keep up — and can't make enough insulin to keep your blood glucose at normal levels. Being overweight, being inactive, or having an unhealthy diet can stop insulin from working.

During pregnancy — usually around the 24th week — many women develop **gestational diabetes**. A diagnosis of gestational diabetes doesn't mean that you had diabetes before you conceived, or that you will have diabetes after giving birth. But it's important to follow your doctor's advice regarding blood sugar levels while you're planning your pregnancy, so you and your baby both remain healthy.

Symptoms

The American Diabetes Association notes that the following symptoms of diabetes are typical. But get yourself checked: some people with type 2 diabetes have symptoms so mild that they go unnoticed:

— Frequent urination
— Feeling very thirsty
— Feeling very hungry, even though you're eating
— Extreme fatigue
— Blurry vision
— Cuts and bruises that are slow to heal
— Weight loss, even though you're eating more (type 1)
— Tingling, pain, or numbness in the hands and feet (type 2)

Diabetics must monitor their levels of blood sugar regularly, and must keep it within a healthy range by being very careful about what they eat and weigh, getting enough exercise and sleep, keeping their blood pressure down, never smoking, and sometimes taking injections of insulin. It's not pleasant to have to take these injections, and for those who are treating the disease really, really well, they may not need medication.

Nutrition means health

The part of this you can control is to arm yourself with a proper diet, which provides a natural protection against fluctuating levels of blood sugar.

As the American Diabetes Association says, you will not necessarily develop type 2 diabetes automatically if you have prediabetes — blood glucose levels that are higher

186

than normal but not yet high enough to be diagnosed as diabetes. For some people with prediabetes, early treatment can actually return blood glucose levels to the normal range.

So help yourself out: research shows that you can lower your risk for type 2 diabetes by 58 percent by losing 7 percent of your body weight (or 15 pounds if you weigh 200 pounds), and exercising moderately (such as brisk walking) 30 minutes a day, five days a week.

With exercise comes nutrition, and here the focus is on protein, an especially important component of all of our diets, but a diabetic's diet in particular. Proteins perform a vast array of functions within living organisms, from catalyzing metabolic reactions to replicating DNA, responding to stimuli, and transporting molecules from site to site.

And where that protein *comes from* plays a role in our overall health: getting your protein from vegetable and lean, all-natural animal sources is far more healthful to patients who suffer from diabetes.

The difference between a typical American diet and a nutritious diet is striking. While the former is laden with saturated fat, fatty animal protein, simple carbohydrate, and over-processed vegetables, the latter offers filling plant and grain products, and lean, all-natural meat protein, and focuses on easily digestible and nutrient-rich food choices.

A delicious new world

Often when we think of the foods diabetics should eat we think of bland, boring foods, and that's unfortunate, as it's no longer true. Modern diabetes diet management invites more fruits, vegetables, and whole grains — foods high in nutrition and low in fat and calories — and fewer animal products and sweets.

Indeed, protein, complex carbohydrates from grains, fruits, vegetables, and fiber are the cornerstones of the ideal diet for diabetics.

Fiber is a particularly important component that helps keep the digestive tract in good shape. Avoid white bread or canned vegetables, as those simple carbohydrates provide hardly any fiber, and actually increase glucose levels. Whole grains, such as found in multigrain bread, and fresh produce are far superior choices to maintain desired levels, due to the longer time they take to pass through the body.

Consume sugars — both processed and natural — only in moderation.

Spread it out

For best results in treating diabetes, eat small meals several times a day rather than large meals three times a day. Deprived of the appropriate levels of proteins and sugars on a regular basis, a diabetic's system will suffer, and complications will set in quickly.

Diabetics also tend to suffer from ill effects of inactive muscles, as their bodies become less sensitive to their usual dose of insulin. As such, just the slightest decrease in appropriate food consumption can spell big trouble for the diabetic.

A balanced vegetable-protein-based diet actually allows for larger food portions, so you'll feel more pleasantly full than if you ate a diet of meat-and-fat-laden, high-animal protein so readily available in today's culture.

Sure, chowing down on a 20-ounce steak will make you feel full, but it'll also make you sluggish, listless, and prone to lack of concentration. The reason is clear: a great deal of blood is sent to the digestive tract to begin the difficult process of breaking that stuff down. Eating such complex, high-fat, calorie-dense food is expensive — not just on your bill, but in terms of what it costs you to process it metabolically.

A nutritious and varied food plan of balanced diets allows diabetics — and everyone else — to consume a number of different, satisfying, long-lasting foods that provide the needed complex carbohydrates and plant proteins we need to keep natural control over glucose levels.

What we recommend

Given the fact that our ancestors thrived on nothing more than fresh meat, nuts, berries, roots, and other foods derived from the earth, it stands to reason that the most effective diabetic diet was with us from the beginning. Only since the industrial revolution have we suffered such dire health issues as heart disease, high blood pressure, and diabetes, all suspiciously coincidental with the introduction of processed grains and sugar. Avoid them.

Supplements help too

With diet and exercise, diabetics and others are successfully relying on supplementation to help control their blood sugars. Below is a list of supplements shown to benefit those with diabetes. A heads-up: for your safety, always look for the Natural Product Association's certification for good manufacturing practices when you buy from any company selling supplements. Your doctor might recommend additional supplements:

— Krill or fish oil, essential source of omega-3 fatty acids, for heart health and to decrease inflammation

— Gender-specific multivitamin, to ensure you meet your daily vitamin and mineral requirements

— Ubiquinol or CoQ10, pure form of antioxidants to boost immune system and manage chronic disease

— Super greens and/or resveratrol, a pure form of antioxidants

— Calcium, magnesium, and potassium

— Chromium chelate

— Cinnamon

We know regular exercise and a balanced healthy eating plan are essential for managing and preventing diabetes. A balanced diet incorporates myriad foodstuffs providing adequate nutrition, calorie control, and variety. If you're taking charge of your diet, and it includes this rich variety of nutrients our bodies depend on, you should find yourself in excellent shape moving forward.

Whatever you do, move forward deliberately, making sensible decisions every step of the way. Try, but don't worry if you can't get to your ideal body weight. As the American Diabetes Association says, losing even 10 to 15 pounds can make a huge difference.

And you have that within your power right now.

References

Bolderman, Karen M. and Mersey, James H. (1996, September). Faithful fasting with diabetes. Diabetes Forecast 49, 48 (3).

Department of Diabetes and Endocrinology, Royal Surrey County Hospital, Guildford, Surrey, U.K.

Green, Moss (2009) Best Diabetic Diet for Diabetes Prevention. Retrieved March 10, 2009, from http://www.bellaonline.com/articles/art43931.asp

Russell-Jones, David, and Khan, Rehman. (2007) Insulin associated weight gain in diabetes – causes, effects, and coping strategies. Diabetes Obes Metab. 9:799-812.

National Institute of Diabetes and Digestive and Kidney Diseases (NIDDK, 2008). Binge Eating Disorder. Retrieved March 10, 2009, from http://win.niddk.nih.gov/publications/binge.htm

Olendzki, B, Speed, C, and Domino FJ/ (2006) Nutritional assessment and counseling for prevention and treatment of cardiovascular disease. Am Fam Physician.

Heart Health and Nutrition: Eat to Beat the Odds

DR. KEITH KANTOR, N.D., PH.D.

HEART DISEASE IS THE LEADING CAUSE OF DEATH for both men and women in the United States, and it's largely preventable. Will we choose to prevent it among our employees? Among the members we serve in our organizations? In our homes?

According to the Mayo Clinic, heart disease is a broad term used to describe a range of diseases that affect your heart. The various diseases that fall under the umbrella of heart disease include diseases of your blood vessels, such as coronary artery disease; heart rhythm problems (arrhythmias); heart infections; and heart defects you're born with (congenital heart defects).

The term "heart disease" is often used interchangeably with "cardiovascular disease." Cardiovascular disease generally refers to conditions that involve narrowed or blocked blood vessels that can lead to a heart attack, chest pain (angina), or stroke. Other heart conditions, such as infections and conditions that affect your heart's muscle, valves, or beating rhythm, also are considered forms of heart disease. [1]

188

Fortunately, many forms of heart disease can be prevented or treated with healthy lifestyle choices. Studies of people with heart disease have shown that lowering high cholesterol and high blood pressure through diet and other means can reduce the risk of nonfatal heart attack or stroke, incidents of heart bypass surgery or angioplasty, and death.

Research on nutrition and heart health proves that certain foods can reduce cholesterol and manage high blood pressure. It's as simple as being clear with ourselves about what we're eating and what we expect will come of it.

Here are a few things you can do today, right now, to manage your cholesterol and reduce your risk of heart attacks, stroke, and a too-sudden end:

• Reduce abdominal fat by having a waist circumference less than 40 inches for men and 35 inches for women. Get out that measuring tape. Don't beat yourself up about whatever number you get; this is your starting point.

• Avoid excessive weight gain. Make sensible decisions every time you eat. Balance calorie expenditure and intake through regular exercise and food portion control. When you consume more calories than you use, you gain weight; when you burn more calories than you take in, you lose weight. (Fortunately, Green Box Foods offers individually wrapped meats and fish to help you control your portions when cooking.)

• Exercise every day. This will help raise HDL, the healthy cholesterol, and give your blood sugar something to do other than build up and poison you.

• Don't smoke. If you were a smoker before opening this book, this is your signal from above that you should quit. Get the support you need by embracing a smoking cessation program today. The American Lung Association's Freedom From Smoking® group clinic includes eight sessions and features a step-by-step plan for quitting smoking. Each session is designed to help smokers gain control over their behavior. The clinic format encourages participants to work on the process and problems of quitting both individually and as part of a group.

Go a step beyond and be a hero: become involved with the Freedom From Smoking® program by either bringing it to your organization or becoming a trained clinic facilitator.

• Enjoy five to 10 servings of fruits and vegetables rich in antioxidants with your daily diet: raspberries, blueberries, and tomatoes are fantastic options, but so are many of the foods described in this book. Moreover, Green Box Foods offers USDA All-natural and organic frozen fruits and vegetables to help you maintain a natural, healthy diet.

• Avoid consuming trans fats, typically found in processed foods with a long shelf life. Get buy-in from your housemates and toss out any food product that comes in a package — and remember this when you shop. Let in only what helps you live healthfully; reject the rest as garbage.

• Consume at least 25 grams of soluble fiber per day. Fiber binds to the bile acids in the bloodstream and scrub away the bad cholesterol that otherwise could clog you up and kill you.

• Consume whole grains; avoid processed and refined grains. There is a difference: Again, the Mayo Clinic: "Also called cereals, grains and whole grains are the seeds of grasses cultivated for food. Grains and whole grains come in many shapes and sizes, from large kernels of popcorn to small quinoa seeds.

"Whole grains are unrefined grains that haven't had their bran and germ removed by milling. Whole grains are better sources of fiber and other important nutrients, such as selenium, potassium and magnesium. Whole grains are either single foods, such as brown rice and popcorn, or ingredients in products, such as buckwheat in pancakes or whole wheat in bread.

"Refined grains. Refined grains are milled, a process that strips out both the bran and germ to give them a finer texture and extend their shelf life. The refining process also removes many nutrients, including fiber. Refined grains include white flour, white rice, white bread and degermed cornflower. Many breads, cereals, crackers, desserts and pastries are made with refined grains, too.

"Enriched grains. Enriched means that some of the nutrients lost during processing are added back in. Some enriched grains are grains that have lost B vitamins added back in — but not the lost fiber. Fortifying means adding in nutrients that don't occur naturally in the food. Most refined grains are enriched, and many enriched grains also are fortified with other vitamins and minerals, such as folic acid and iron. Some countries require certain refined grains to be enriched. Whole grains may or may not be fortified." [2]

• Limit alcohol. From the American Heart Association: "If you drink alcohol, do so in moderation. This means an average of one to two drinks per day for men and one drink per day for women. (A drink is one 12 oz. beer, 4 oz. of wine, 1.5 oz. of 80-proof spirits, or 1 oz. of 100-proof spirits.) Drinking more alcohol increases such dangers as alcoholism, high blood pressure, obesity, stroke, breast cancer, suicide and accidents. Also, it's not possible to predict in which people alcoholism will become a problem."

• Get the facts about your body. See your doctor for an annual checkup. Your doctor knows you and can help you make a lasting, measurable, effective plan to prevent lifestyle diseases. It's better that then seeing him (or her) only in the hospital after the damage is done.

Live like you mean it with a heart-healthy diet

Now that you know the immediate steps you can take toward better heart health, let's look more closely at the food choices you can make to meet your goal of living better, happier, longer, and with more money in your pocket.

One of the best things you can do for your heart is eating a heart-friendly diet such as the Dietary Approaches to Stop Hypertension (DASH) eating plan. Following the DASH diet (www.dashdiet.org), eat foods that are low in fat, cholesterol, and salt, and rich in fruits, vegetables, whole grains, and low-fat dairy products that can help protect your heart. Legumes, low-fat sources of protein and certain types of fish, also can reduce your risk of heart disease.

Smarten up on fats

• Know the differences among saturated, polyunsaturated, monounsaturated, and trans fats. Saturated fats and trans fats increase the risk of coronary artery disease by raising blood cholesterol levels.

• Major sources of saturated fat include non-lean beef, butter, cheese, and milk, and coconut and palm oils. Keep in mind that Green Box Foods (www.greenboxfoods.com) offers a DASH-ideal variety of lean, natural, hormone-free meats and seafood.

• Growing evidence shows that trans fat may be worse for you than saturated fat. Unlike saturated fat, trans fat both raises your low-density lipoprotein (LDL), or "bad" cholesterol, and lowers your high-density lipoprotein (HDL), or "good" cholesterol.

Sources of trans fat include some deep-fried fast foods, bakery products, packaged snack foods, margarine, and crackers. Read your food labels: if you see "partially hydrogenated" listed, that's trans fat, and it wants to hurt you.

The good fat — Omega-3 fatty acids

That's not to say all fat is dangerous. We're supposed to take on certain fats. Omega-3 fatty acids, for example, are polyunsaturated fats our bodies can't synthesize but nevertheless depend on for normal metabolism. Actually referring to a group of three fats called ALA (found in plant oils), EPA, and DHA (both commonly found in marine oils), omega-3s also decrease our risk of heart attack, protect against irregular heartbeats, and lower blood pressure.

Some fish, such as salmon and halibut, are great natural sources of omega-3 fatty acids, as are flax seeds, walnuts, soybeans, shrimp, tofu, and winter squash.

Green Box Foods always provides its customers with a wide variety of fresh seafood, fruits, and vegetables, all full of omega-3 fatty acids and of wonderful benefit to your heart. Omega-3s:

• Reduce the factors leading to body-wide inflammation and hardening of the arteries

• Keep your blood from clotting excessively

• Increase the activity of another natural chemical that helps arteries relax and let blood flow unimpeded

• Maintain the fluidity of your cell membranes

• Lower the amount of lipids — bad fats such as cholesterol and triglycerides — circulating in your bloodstream

• Reduce the risk of obesity

• Improve the body's ability to respond to insulin, which helps regulate food intake, body weight, and metabolism

• Help prevent the growth of cancer cells

Note that pregnant women and women of childbearing age should avoid shark, swordfish, king mackerel, and tilefish, as these contain levels of environmental mercury sufficient to pose a danger to a developing fetus.

For most other folks, the health benefits of fish outweigh any risks associated with mercury.

Take the right supplements

Omega-3s are present in smaller amounts in flaxseed oil, walnut oil, soybean oil, and canola oil, and they can also be found in supplements. Research has also shown that those who eat right, exercise, and take advantage of supplementation see better results compared with those who don't use supplements.

Because they work, omega-3 supplements are recommended in addition to a heart-healthy diet. Make sure you get them from manufacturers advertising the Natural Products Association "NPA Natural Seal" or TruLabel® for good manufacturing practices. You want to get enough:

— Krill or fish oil, an essential source of omega-3 fatty acids

— Gender-specific multivitamin

— Ubiquinol or CoQ10

— Super greens and/or resveratrol

— Additional supplements as your doctor recommends

The best prescription for heart health is a healthy diet, regular exercise, non-smoking lifestyle, and alcohol only in moderation. Do that and you should be in good shape. Don't forget to stack the deck in your favor with heart-healthy omega-3 fatty acid supplements. For more information, visit www.greenboxfoods.com.

References

1. www.mayoclinic.com/health/heart-disease, accessed 8/7/2013

2. www.mayoclinic.com/health/whole-grains, accessed 8/7/2013

Obesity and Nutrition

DANA YARN, R.D., L.D., AND DR. KEITH KANTOR, N.D., PH.D.

THE AMERICAN MEDICAL ASSOCIATION IN 2013 finally declared obesity a disease, a decision that effectively defines 78 million American adults and 12 million children as having a medical condition requiring treatment.

Doctors can treat obesity and its heavily correlated lifestyle diseases at great expense to patients and the economy, but it's easier for all of us to prevent obesity in the first place. And that begins with educating ourselves about what we're eating, what we need to eat to feel at our best, and how to support our bodies so that they can support us.

We need to do certain things better at a minimum: get enough sleep, drink enough water, get enough exercise, and eat a rich variety of all-natural foods. If we do that much for our families and ourselves, well ... problem solved. That would be the end of the story.

The problem of being overweight in the United States has escalated to great proportions over the last several decades. Obesity leads to heart disease, diabetes, and other preventable chronic illnesses. Recent studies have shown that obesity has just edged out smoking as the leading cause of death in our country. And we're doing it to ourselves.

Fat itself is good for us ... within reason

Let's start here: our bodies are designed to store extra energy in the form of fat, as food wasn't always so plentiful as our species was developing. Life was much more physically demanding for our kind of animal, and without these reserves, we might simply starve, or at least not quite thrive. Fat is meant as a temporary advantage to see us through the lean times — not as a lifestyle.

And fat does help us in other ways: vitamins A, D, E, and K are fat-soluble, meaning they can only be digested, absorbed, and transported in conjunction with fats. Fats are also sources of essential fatty acids, an important dietary requirement.

They also play a vital role in maintaining healthy skin and hair, insulating body organs against shock, maintaining body temperature, and promoting healthy cell function.

We also know fat serves as a useful buffer against a host of diseases, protecting vital organs until such time as an offending substance in fat cells' grip can be metabolized or eliminated.

We're not calling for you to remove fat from your diet completely, even if you could. Doing so would be unhealthy. Some fatty acids are essential nutrients, meaning that they can't be produced in the body from other compounds and need to be consumed in small amounts.

But fat to the point of obesity? That's bad. And that you can, and must, control and prevent. Why wouldn't you?

When the pants don't fit and we wheeze

A greater number of Americans than ever certainly know what it feels like to be obese. Being overweight or obese is defined as having excess body fat, a weight that is greater than what is considered healthy for your given height. In terms of numbers, being obese is having a Body Mass Index (BMI) of greater than 30; morbid obesity is having a BMI greater than 40.

Here's how to calculate your BMI: multiply your weight in pounds by 703, and divide that number by your height in inches squared. (There are, of course, numerous websites that will calculate your BMI with a few mouse clicks.)

Nowadays, high-calorie food is everywhere, and because we still seek out the salty, fatty, and sugary foods our taste buds readily respond to — they're still under the impression energy-rich foods are scarce, and they're trying to help you survive in the wilderness — we're now wallowing in the stuff, and are significantly less active than we need to be. We're drowning in fat, poisoning our cells, and letting our muscles turn to mush.

And in treating the symptoms of these diseases, we're wasting trillions of dollars, money our country — our children and grandchildren — can't afford. According to the government, poor nutrition is a significant driver of the American workforce's health issues. Lower obesity rates alone could result in productivity gains of $254 billion and avoid $60 billion in treatment expenditures per year.

So here's what you can do right now: understand that body weight has several influences: genes, metabolism, muscle mass, behavior, support system, culture activity and socioeconomic status. The greatest areas of obesity prevention are within your behavior and your environment.

In other words, you are in control of your weight right now: if you're sleepwalking through life, it's time to wake up and take charge. This is vital for you and your family to recognize. Nine times out of ten, people are overweight because they choose to be. With little exception, obesity is a voluntary disease.

The facts:

— Obesity is an AMA-certified epidemic in this country.

— It is directly related to the increase of chronic diseases such as heart disease, hypertension, and cancer.

— More than 60 million American adults are obese; the condition accounts for two-thirds of diabetes and heart disease victims, and contributes to 15 percent of cancer in women and 20 percent in men.

— Obesity can also cause disabilities, pain, and suffering, and may negatively affect mobility and other quality-of-life measures.

You can take charge of your weight today. Fortunately, eating well and exercising — everything we talk about in this book — is pretty much guaranteed to stem your weight woes.

When attempting to eat a healthier, more natural diet:

— Avoid processed foods packed with high-fructose corn syrup and other chemical preservatives that promote unhealthy blood sugar levels and fat buildup in the arteries.

— Surround yourself with health-minded people who'll aid you on your quest to become fitter and more health conscious. Seek these people out. A healthy support system that encourages healthy eating and physical activity — whether it comes from the government, employers, or the love of family and friends — will help prevent or cure obesity. But we must take responsibility for our own actions.

— Stop supporting businesses and brands that only serve to fatten you up for the kill.

— Recognize that a processed food is anything that comes in a packaging of any sort. Toss out those Ho Hos! Focus on eating a plant-based diet, incorporating lean protein sources such as fish or chicken breast and whole grains, such as oatmeal, brown rice, and high fiber/low sugar cereals.

— Dine out less, and cook from home more. The oversized portions, hidden calories, fat, sodium, and sugar in restaurant or cafeteria food pack weight on us. Brown-bagging it allows you to control precisely what you consume. If you must dine out, order healthier options such as soups and salads, with dressing on the side.

— Supplement your diet. In order to treat obesity, you'll need to reduce your caloric intake, which, if attempted haphazardly, could lead to nutrition deficiencies. This is where supplementation can help you lose weight

192

without putting your health at risk. Supplements also increase weight-loss progress more than diet and exercise alone. Make sure your supplements manufacturer is certified by the Natural Products Association.

Here are several supplements we recommend for those trying to lose weight and fight diseases related to obesity:

— Krill or fish oil, essential sources of omega-3 fatty acids

— Gender-specific multivitamins to meet daily vitamin and mineral requirements

— Ubiquinol or CoQ10, a pure form of antioxidants to boost the immune system and manage chronic disease

— Probiotics for digestive and immune health

— Super greens and/or resveratrol, a pure form of antioxidants

— Branch-chain amino acids (for those who work out regularly) to increase muscle recovery after workouts

— Calcium/magnesium/potassium, for bone health

— Ginseng and green tea as a natural-energy and metabolic booster

By making these commonsense changes in your daily diet and activity schedule, you're sure to slim down and improve your overall health.

And you can do it all without spending even one minute in a doctor's office or paying a single cent to an insurance company. And you'll feel at home in your skin and in your clothes again.

References

R. Kuczmarski et al., Increasing prevalence of overweight among U.S, adults," JAMA 272 (1994): 205-11.

G. Kolata, "Why do people get fat?" Science 227 (1985): 1327-28.

R.J. Wurtman and J.J. Wurtman, "Brain Serotonin, Carbohydrate-Craving, Obesity and Depression,"Adv Exp Med Biol 398 (1996) 35-41.

Salt, Salt-Free, and Salt Substitutes

Know your options for fantastic meals and lasting heart health

DANA YARN, R.D., L.D., AND
DR. KEITH KANTOR, N.D., PH.D.

JUST THE RIGHT AMOUNT OF SALT ADDED TO A RECIPE pleasantly draws out a food's flavor and makes meals more enjoyable. Beyond taste, we do need sodium to live: this essential nutrient, which sits outside of our cell membranes, assists in transmitting nerve impulses, influences the contraction and relaxation of muscles, and helps maintain the proper blood volume.

Again, that's just the right amount. Just as too little dietary sodium is dangerous, excessive dietary salt is deadly, and here's why: when excess sodium builds up in the body, it draws not taste, but rather water molecules out of the cells and into the bloodstream. Now you're dealing with hypertension: excess sodium overfills the blood with water, and our circulatory systems labor that much harder to pump everything along. Try carrying a full water cooler jug around for a day or thirty, and you'll begin to appreciate the kind of stress to which too much water subjects your heart and arteries. Serious heart problems are not far off.

And that's for otherwise healthy people. Those with ailments, or precursors for ailments such congestive heart failure, cirrhosis, and chronic kidney disease, will already find it difficult for their kidneys to balance sodium levels in the body. Should increased blood pressure turn chronic, it can lead to — and worsen — heart disease, stroke, kidney disease, and congestive heart failure.

What's worse, prolonged excessive salt consumption — beyond what our bodies pluck from salt that's found naturally in what we eat — conditions the taste buds to expect it in our meals: we need more and more to "feel" we're getting enough, and that can lead us to consume far more sodium than our recommended daily allowance. There are alternatives, about which we'll say more shortly.

First, here are some helpful facts about sodium:

— The 2010 Dietary Guidelines for Americans recommend limiting sodium to less than 2,300 mg a day, or 1,500 mg if you're age 51 or older; have family history of heart disease; or have high blood pressure, diabetes, or chronic kidney disease.

— The average American gets 3,400 mg or more of sodium per day, far more then the recommended amount. Sodium doesn't just come from the kitchen saltshaker; it's also found in many foods that you may not realize are high in sodium (so check those labels).

— Processed and prepared foods contain high sodium levels, as they're processed to last for a long period and sodium typically is the main preservative. Such foods include frozen prepared meals, pizza, cold cuts, and soups, unless they're specified to be low in sodium.

— Some foods have higher sodium content naturally: cottage cheese, milk, and shellfish, for example. One serving of milk contains more than 200 mg of sodium.

— Sodium adds up when you're cooking and using condiments. For example, one tablespoon of teriyaki sauce contains more than 1,000 mg of sodium. Ketchup, too, packs in a large amount

What's in a name?

Some people say they're confused by the variety of names salt is marketed under, including sea salt, table salt, and kosher salt. Here's a little background you might find helpful in making heart-healthy choices that taste great too.

Sea salt. Also known as bay salt or solar salt, this is simply produced from the evaporation of seawater. It's primarily sodium chloride; arrives in large, coarse crystals; and is relatively expensive. To its credit, sea salt does contain more minerals than table salt, which is much

more heavily processed, but the mineral content varies depending on its source.

We believe sea salt tastes better, and has a better texture, than ordinary table salt. Some recipes call for sea salt because of its coarse texture: it can provide a different mouth feel, and may change flavor due to its different rate of dissolution.

Our greatest concern with sea salt — beyond that we consume too much salt generally — is that industry has polluted the seas to the point where we've polluted this naturally derived seasoning. Efforts are made to clean salt before it's shipped, but you don't want to add pollutants to your food or body in any volume.

Table salt. Table salt is as much salt as sea salt is, but by the time it reaches market it's been stripped, processed, bleached, and given additives: anti-clumping agents to help it flow easily from saltshakers, sugar to protect the anti-caking agents, and other stabilizers.

And there are some minerals in table salt that the body just can't absorb, and so they sit around in deposits and blockages in the body.

Koshering salt, usually referred to as kosher salt in the U.S., is a variety of edible salt with a much larger grain size than some common table salt. Like common table salt, kosher salt consists of sodium chloride.

Unlike some common table salt, however, kosher salt typically contains no additives, such as iodine, although some brands include small amounts of anticlumping agents. (You can also get additive-free nonkosher salt.)

Kosher salt sounds good, and has its place, but it isn't right for everything or everybody. Cooks know that kosher salt generally is not recommended for baking with recipes that use small amounts of wet ingredients. Lacking enough liquid, kosher salt won't dissolve well, leaving small bits of salt crystal lingering in the resulting product.

Because salt grain types can vary in size considerably from one brand to another, check the box for a conversion guideline. If you don't see one, twice as much kosher salt (by volume) generally replaces table salt in recipes — or just use an equal weight — but again, you don't need this much sodium chloride.

Enjoy going salt-free

As vital as salt is for our blood chemistry and metabolism, and given that Americans consume too much of it beyond what we get from our diet naturally, we see sodium chloride as a thing to limit or avoid. Try going salt-free, and look for that assurance on nutrition labels.

Have fun with it: start experimenting with other, more flavorful herbs and spices to add zip to your meals. Fresh garlic or garlic powder, lemon juice, flavored vinegar, salt-free herb blends, cumin, nutmeg, cinnamon, fresh ground pepper, tarragon, oregano, and many others work as well or better to complement foods' natural flavors.

Enjoy salt substitutes as part of a healthy diet

Almost as well, you can certainly achieve success with salt substitutes, low-sodium table salt alternatives. As health care providers, we've been slow to warm to salt substitutes: just as table salt is composed of sodium chloride and strains the body when consumed in excess, salt substitutes add, or are chiefly composed of, potassium chloride, which itself strains the kidneys and heart when consumed in excess.

But the saving grace of some salt substitutes is that the recommended daily allowance of potassium is greater than that for sodium, so we find room in a healthy diet for these alternatives. People in good health should strongly consider a recommended salt substitute; those with kidney failure, heart failure, or diabetes should not take salt substitutes without medical advice.

So which do we recommend? We like two brands for their taste, production practices, and nutritional value:

AlsoSalt (www.alsosalt.com) is superior to mainstream salt substitutes for several reasons, and this is why our companies now provide it to our clients:

— Unlike most salt substitutes, AlsoSalt doesn't have a metallic aftertaste, as it contains the amino acid lysine, which acts as a taste enhancer. Lysine, an essential amino acid, is one our bodies can't produce, so we have to supply it through diet.

— AlsoSalt contains half the potassium of mainstream brands, which decreases strain on the kidneys and heart. You can reliably cook, bake, and season with it, but just like table salt, this is best used in moderation.

Original Himalayan Crystal Salt (www.himalayancrystalsalt.com) is for those who aren't necessarily under doctor's orders to avoid salt, but who choose to avoid it anyway, knowing the health risks. This natural product has numerous health benefits, and is far superior to table salt and even sea salt.

We provide our clients Original Himalayan Crystal Salt because it contains 84 trace minerals in nearly the same ratios naturally found in our blood. The crystal minerals found in Himalayan Crystal Salt are in ionic form, meaning they are electrically charged and absorb directly into a cell, instead of relying on transport through the blood stream, as our bodies do with nutrients delivered by food.

The salts are derived from the Himalayan mountain range, home to some of the planet's highest peaks, including the highest, Mount Everest, and are the mineral salt crystals created there 250 million years ago. A legacy of ancient oceans, trapped after tectonic plate movement and subsequent evaporation, Himalayan Crystal Salt contains dozens of minerals vital for human health, such as sodium, chloride, potassium, calcium, magnesium, iodine, iron, zinc, and manganese.

Moreover, because of this product's balanced crystalline structure, it's easily metabolized in the body, resulting in a net *gain* of the body's energy and resources.

When we consider the depleted mineral reserves in soils, non-sustainable farming practices, and pesticides that inhibit the uptake of certain minerals, humans are unable to depend on quite the wealth minerals we once found in vegetables, fruit, and animal products, particularly in the supermarket, and that's unfortunate.

Go salt-free, or sprinkle in a moderate amount of recommended salt substitute: a natural way to replenish essential minerals, give your heart and arteries a fighting chance, and ensure yourself a good, long life.

References

Livestrong: http://www.livestrong.org

Dr. Gourmet's Food Reviews: http://www.drgourmet.com/newsletter/reviews/092807.shtml

Mayo Clinic: http://www.mayoclinic.com/health/sodium/NU00284

Original Himalayan Crystal Salt®: http://www.himalayancrystalsalt.com/clinical-research.html

Saldanha, Carlin, N.D., MPH. Why the right salt is essential to your health: Comparing table salt, sea salt, and Himalayan Crystal salt.

Make Mealtime a Family Time

DANA YARN, R.D., L.D., AND
DR. KEITH KANTOR, N.D., Ph.D.

WHEN MEALTIME IS FAMILY TIME, KIDS FEEL great about their contribution, and grown-ups know they're helping guide a generation of healthy, active, involved young people. Even preschoolers can do a lot, with the proper supervision to start, and you can build on their skills every year.

They can:

— Give their opinion about which vegetables they'd like with which proteins and carbs. (If they say they don't like *any*, then give them a choice between two or three, making sure your options include a good variety, which you can change every week)

— Help you pick out the tastiest-looking produce

— Set the table

— Take foods out of grocery bags, refrigerator, or pantry

— Wash fruits and vegetables (naming them as they go)

— Read recipes

— Set the timer, and report on how much time is left

— Measure ingredients

— Stir ingredients in a bowl

— Spread or layer ingredients in a pan before baking

— Help clear the table and wash and dry dishes

— Join in a high-five because they helped contribute to a fun, safe, and yummy mealtime

Make family meals enjoyable

As kids get older, they can take on a whole lot more, from menu planning to cooking, and even talking about how food is prepared and enjoyed in other homes and other cultures. And they'll do so knowing their choices about food are just that — choices they can make for a good, long life.

These tips, "Make Mealtime a Family Time," come to us from the USDA "Choose My Plate" website. We hope you put them to work and enjoy the result:

— Start eating meals together as a family when your kids are young. This way, it becomes a habit.

— Plan when you will eat together as a family. Write it on your calendar.

— You may not be able to eat together every day. Try to have family meals most days of the week.

— Focus on the meal and each other. Turn off the television. Take phone calls or texts later.

— Talk about fun and happy things. Try to make meals a stress-free time.

— Encourage your child to try foods. But don't lecture or force your child to eat.

— Involve your child in conversation. Ask questions like:

— What made you feel really happy today?

— What did you have to eat at lunch today?

— What's your favorite veggie? Why?

— Tell me one thing you learned today.

— What made you laugh today?

—Have your child help you get ready to eat. Depending on age, your child may be able to:

— Help set the table

— Put pets, toys, or books in another room

— Turn off the TV

— Pour milk (with help)

— Put down place mats

— Hand out napkins and silverware

— Pick flowers for the table

— Clear the table

— Wipe the table

Ideas for fast family meals

— Cook it fast on busy nights. Try stir-fried meat and vegetables, quick soups, sandwiches, or quesadillas.

— Do some tasks the day before. Wash and cut vegetables or make a fruit salad. Cook lean ground beef or turkey for burritos or chili. Store everything in the fridge until ready to use.

— Find quick and tasty recipes that don't cost a lot to make.

Remember, it's not just today's meal or snack you're making: it's also tomorrow's memories.

Source

www.choosemyplate.gov/preschoolers/healthy-habits/making-mealtime-family-time.html

Set a Good Example

DANA YARN, R.D., L.D., AND DR. KEITH KANTOR, N.D., PH.D.

YOUR CHILD PICKS UP ALL OF YOUR ATTITUDES and behaviors, including your eating habits: your table manners, likes and dislikes, willingness to try new foods, and physical activities. These tips from the United States Department of Agriculture make a great guide to help you improve on the whole family's mealtime home game:

Eat together. Eat meals with your child whenever possible. Let your child see you enjoying fruits, vegetables, and whole grains at meals and snacks.

Take it with you. Show your child how to make healthy choices when you are on the run. Put oranges, bananas, or other fruits in your bag for quick snacks. Let your child see that you like to munch on vegetables when you're on the go.

Share the adventure. Be willing to try new foods, and try new foods together.

Cook together. Encourage your preschooler to help you prepare meals and snacks. Teach your child to tear lettuce or add veggie toppings to pizza. Cooking together can mean more "mommy (or daddy) and me" time on busy days.

Keep things positive. Discourage older children and other family members from making yucky faces or negative comments about unfamiliar foods.

Set a good example for physical activity, too. Make play time a family time. Walk, run, and play with your child rather than sit on the sidelines.

Source

www.choosemyplate.gov/preschoolers/healthy-habits/set-a-good-example.html

Understanding Exercise and Its Role in Health

DANA YARN, R.D., L.D., AND
DR. KEITH KANTOR, N.D, PH.D.

IDEALLY, WE'D ALL START OUT AS HEALTHY, ACTIVE KIDS and never lose the thrill of moving our bodies in strenuous, rewarding play. That's what exercise wants to be for us, though many of us lose touch with that as we get older, and we feel guilty — we "have to" exercise or "should" get more exercise — and because we've dropped it from our lifestyle, we feel it's hard to fit back in.

Good news: it's never too late to move with a kid's enthusiasm for life. It's never too late to correct years — decades, in some cases — of sedentary living that, with poor nutrition, not enough sleep, and not enough water, has led to chronic, expensive illness and discomfort.

Physical fitness and overall health and wellness are in your control right now. Give yourself permission to live the way you remember feeling most happy and alive. Be a kid again, and move your body. For all the years to come you'll grow fit, well, and whole, ready for all the challenges and celebrations life brings, and with an inner glow and a ready smile. It's that easy.

Physical exercise, alone, in a club, or with friends, strengthens muscles and the cardiovascular system; hones athletic skills; provides weight loss or maintenance; boosts the immune system, confidence, and body image; helps prevent Alzheimer's disease, cardiovascular disease, depression, type 2 diabetes, heart disease, and obesity — and is fun: it's you at your best.

So you know that. And because you're reading this book you've already started making positive changes for yourself. Great job. This is the next step: understand the types of exercise you have at your disposal, and keep putting them to work: cardiovascular exercise, strength training, and flexibility training.

Cardiovascular exercise is physical exercise of relatively low intensity, which uses oxygen to meet the body's energy demands, and can be performed for extended periods. Examples: running, purposeful walking, swimming, cycling, and dancing. All of this improves your cardiovascular/ heart health, builds endurance, and burns fat and calories, helping to manage weight.

• Use a heart rate monitor: tracking your effort is a great accountability tool that'll help keep you honest and on track to meeting your goals. The exercise intensity should be between 60 percent and 85 percent of your maximum heart rate. Take it a step further and ask your doctor or trainer to get you a metabolic assessment profile to more accurately understand how your body burns fat, and how your heart processes oxygen while exercising.

• Mix it up: As much fun as your favorite activity might be, avoid settling for the same type of cardiovascular activity every time at the same level. Our bodies love a challenge and like to be surprised. The more you condition your cardiovascular system to support you at greater levels, from new directions, the more you'll naturally seek out greater challenges. Walk or jog at a comfortable pace one day, then take on interval training with hills or speed the next. Swim or row to engage different muscles; dance to fast music or slow — and your routine will catch up to you and reward your whole body.

• Go for quality, not quantity: Quality workouts, in the proper, safe, form, are more fun, efficient, and effective than long workouts. After about 40 minutes of exercise your body starts to release cortisol, a stress hormone that could save your life if you were being chased by a tiger but that works against you if you're trying to repair muscle tissue, get a good night's sleep, and digest food. If you exercise for long without proper nutrition or recovery, excessive inflammation from increased cortisol production could lead to weight gain you don't want. Slow and steady wins this race.

198

Strength or resistance training is a type of physical exercise specializing in the use of resistance to induce muscular contraction that builds the strength, anaerobic endurance, and size of skeletal muscles. Anaerobic exercise is brief and intense. The benefits to your metabolism (the chemical, nutrient-fed processes that keep you alive) and disease management and prevention, and anti-aging, are fantastic.

A word about gyms: it's unfortunate that some people associate strength training with gym rats, bulking up, and daunting circuit machines and free weights. Gyms really are support centers for people determined to let their best physical selves shine through. There are amazing, dedicated, friendly folks on staff who know how to help you get the most out of your membership, so introduce yourself today. Another myth: you need to lose a certain amount of weight through cardiovascular exercise before you can start lifting weights. This just isn't so. You can start today.

The metabolic and health benefits of strength training are clear:

• Manage and prevent type 2 diabetes: Strength training won't make up for a diet of poor-quality, high-carb, processed food, but it can help your body process insulin more effectively. According to a new study, those with relatively more muscle mass are less likely to develop prediabetes. [1] Likewise, when we lose blood sugar control through both inactivity and poor nutrition, it's more difficult for the body to burn fat — making it easier to gain weight and harder to lose it.

• Type 2 diabetes is most often diagnosed in those who are in middle and later adulthood, after significant damage is done. As it happens, this is the time in life when we're commonly less active, and have less muscle mass, than we had when we were younger. Because you've decided to make weight training a regular part of your lifestyle today you're on your way to help yourself reduce age-related muscle loss and reverse the damage that could otherwise spell diabetes.

• With resistance training, you'll slow the rate your muscles "age" and help rebuild and repair them, so you'll look and feel more like your younger, healthier self. The sedentary know it's common to lose tone in the areas where we have the most muscle, and gain mass in the areas where we best store fat. And thank goodness our bodies do store fat — they're supposed to, to help us get through the lean months. But modern humans, or modern Westerners, don't really know from lean months, so our fat stores are only getting larger and dragging us down. Weight training powers the machine our bodies need to burn fat and make new, younger-acting and -looking muscle tissue. [2]

• Supercharge your metabolism: It's common for dieters' weight to fluctuate, especially if we achieve that initial weight loss through diet and little exercise. Resistance training has been shown to play an important role in avoiding weight regain. After a weight-training session, our bodies burn calories at a higher metabolic rate for a day or two, increasing metabolism and the amount of calories the body burns at rest. That's right: at rest. Cutting calories by diet alone only slows metabolism, making genuine, sustainable, systemic weight loss a tougher challenge.

• Maintain testosterone levels with age: Conventional medicine accepts the long-held belief that testosterone levels fall as we age, especially in men. Research suggests an observed fall in testosterone levels may be a result of a loss of muscle tissue stemming from a lack of regular strength training.[3] So use it or lose it. It's true that a reduction in testosterone may stem from stress and other conditions as well, but training with weights is an easy way to combat testosterone loss and the overall stress aging brings.

Flexibility training typically consists of yoga, Pilates, meditation, stretching, and physical therapy (or even "prehab" or "rehab" by athletes). This type of training is least used by those looking to shed pounds through exercise, as it's true that it doesn't burn a lot of calories. But for sheer stress relief, adrenal health benefits, and anti-inflammatory benefits, this type of exercise is a gold mine, and does promote long-term health and weight loss.

Think of it as flexibility for mind and body. Stress stimulates the sympathetic nervous system and puts our bodies into overdrive for a long period, releasing excess stress hormones. These days, we tend to overcommit and overschedule our lives, leading to overstimulation of the sympathetic nervous system. This only results in inflammation, high blood pressure, and muscle pain, which leads to more weight gain and worsens symptoms of depression.

To offset the negative health and weight effects of always being in "overdrive," spend a little time consciously stimulating your parasympathetic nervous system by centering the mind and body. You're not looking to over-exert yourself, but to gently trigger your body's natural, restorative relaxation response through an exercise format such as yoga or Pilates.

Meditation has been shown to improve sleep, mood, pain relief, and anxiety. A four-month study of the effects of meditation found positive correlations with most common hormones that influence weight gain, specifically cortisol, testosterone, growth hormone, and thyroid-stimulating hormone. [4]

So exercise. Put yourself to work for you, to feel alive, live longer, and set a great example. Recent clinical studies have shown that those who exercise regularly gain an average of five years over those who don't — and the life you'll enjoy in all the years from now to then will be spent out of the doctor's office and in your own, real, rewarding self.

References

1. The Endocrine Society. Increased muscle mass may lower risk of pre-diabetes: Study shows building muscle can lower person's risk of insulin resistance. ScienceDaily, 28 Jul. 2011. Web. 7 Aug. 2011.

2. Melov S, Tarnopolsky MA, Beckman K, Felkey K, Hubbard A. Resistance Exercise Reverses Aging in Human Skeletal Muscle. PLoS ONE 2007;2(5):e465.doi:10.1371/journal.pone.0000465

3. The Endocrince Society. Older age does not cause testosterone levels to decline in healthy men. EurekAlert! 7 Jun 2011. http://www.eurekalert.org/pub_releases/2011-06/tes-oad060711.php

4. MacLean, CR, et al. "Effects of the Transcendental Meditation program on adaptive mechanisms: changes in hormone levels and responses to stress after 4 months of practice." Pyshoneuroendocrinology 1997 May; 22(4):277-295

The Importance of Quality Sleep on Health and Metabolism

DANA YARN, R.D., L.D., AND
DR. KEITH KANTOR, N.D., PH.D.

SLEEP IS THE BEST MEDICINE FOR OVERALL HEALTH and optimal vitality. How unfortunate that adequate sleep turns out to be our least utilized weight loss and wellness strategy. So often we sacrifice quality sleep for work, late-night television, digestion, and surfing the Web.

That's poor stress management, and it doesn't let our bodies reset, repair, and rebuild from the previous day. We need seven to eight hours of quality sleep per night for optimal health.

And sleep does more than let us wake up refreshed. Abundant research shows a direct correlation between poor sleep and obesity: according to the *Journal of Clinical Endocrinology and Metabolism*, insulin levels and carbohydrate metabolism suffer the day after one poor night's sleep, resulting in excess fat storage and decreased fat burn.

Think about the last time you had a poor night's sleep. How did you eat the next day? You probably woke up cranky, lingered in bed too long, felt disorganized, grabbed some quick carbohydrates and caffeine on your way out the door for a quick energy fix, and were irritable until lunchtime. And then you probably dragged your butt the rest of the day.

Certainly, going one night without deep, restful sleep won't lead to serious psychological or metabolic disorders — but the fact is that so many of us have learned to make do with poor sleep as a matter of routine. The result is poor metabolism, excess weight, and serious metabolic issues such as type 2 diabetes, adrenal fatigue, and insufficient thyroid.

200

The list goes on, particularly as we age, when we tend to get less sleep: now we're susceptible to a direct, increased risk of cancer, brain fog, and dementia.

Finding your best sleep solution has everything to do with understanding and addressing what causes those sleepless nights to begin with. The best way to improve the quality of your sleep is to make small, important changes.

Here's what we recommend as business people, family people, and health care providers:

• Slow down. Answering e-mails and catching up on work off the clock will hardly make you more productive: unplug from your professional commitments when you're at home and winding down.

• Get a handle on stress, either by becoming more organized or adding to your daytime exercise regimen. When you're stressed, your body releases an abundance of the stress hormone cortisol, which puts you in a state of "fight or flight." That suppresses production of melatonin, the sleep hormone, and serotonin, the "good-mood hormone," and dings your ability to get uninterrupted sleep. Meditate, take a yoga class, or simply incorporate activities that bring more joy into your everyday life.

• Power down the electronic gear and social media an hour or two before bedtime. The light from the television affects your body much as the light from the Sun does. Think about how bright the casinos are in Las Vegas: those guys want you up and about (and not thinking clearly) at all hours.

• Most television shows are hardly relaxing: they're designed to keep you in a heightened state of urgency so you'll be ready to take in and act on their advertisers' messages — and they may raise your levels of stress hormones, one of the worst things you can do for your metabolism at night.

• Add a digital video recorder to your cable plan and record your favorite shows for another evening's viewing. Read a book, or just take some time to relax. Over time, you'll reduce the amount of time you spend tossing and turning, and your body will enjoy a restorative night's sleep that will make you more capable the next day — and have less to stress about.

• Keep children's toys, projects, laundry, and other clutter out of your bedroom. Organizational whiz Peter Walsh says the master bedroom has one or two purposes, neither of which should invite children's clutter (and both of which are hampered by it).

• Avoid eating a heavy meal before bed — say, after 7 p.m. — as this puts your digestive system in overdrive, taking resources other parts of your body need for recovery and repair. As well, it's important to eat all-natural foods that contain no harmful chemicals, dyes, preservatives, hormones, or antibiotics. Consuming harmful chemicals decreases sleep quality.

• Ensure you're getting quality nutrients from food and supplementation. Magnesium, part of a core supplementation program of multivitamins, fish oil, and probiotics, has been shown to help against restless leg syndrome. If the body lacks any nutrient, your sleep will be affected.

• Consider supplementing with 5-HTP, a precursor to the important hormones melatonin and serotonin. When those hormones are depleted, it's difficult to fall asleep, and you'll feel excessive sugar and carbohydrate cravings.

• Aim to maintain a cool, dark, and quiet bedroom. Noisy gadgets, pets, and bright lights from clocks or baby monitors can interrupt quality sleep and affect your overall health. Don't sleep with your smartphone or tablet within reach. Clear your brain and report to work the next day refreshed and ready to take care of business.

• Consistency is key. We push our kids to adhere to a specific bedtime; why aren't we as disciplined for our own health? The best time to sleep is between the hours of 10 p.m. and 6 a.m., which correlates with the body's natural rhythm, what's going on outside, and the natural rhythm of sunrise and sunset.

Early to bed, early to rise was Benjamin Franklin's advice. We say get enough sleep so that your body supports you in all the important work you're doing, and all the play you need to support your body. You'll feel better, start your day more confidently, and have sweeter dreams.

References

The Endocrine Society. One Sleepless Night Can Induce Insulin Resistance in Healthy People. Science Daily 5 May 2010 (http://www.sciencedaily.com/releases/2010/05/100505091632.htm)

University of Hafia. Artificial Light at Night Disrupts Cell Division, Research Shows. Science Daily. 20 April 2010 (http://www.sciencedaily.com/releases/2010/04/100412095542.htm)

The Health Dangers of Refined Sugars

DANA YARN, R.D., L.D., AND DR. KEITH KANTOR, N.D., PH.D.

THE SUGAR IN OUR BODIES, GLUCOSE, IS A fundamental fuel for human life. So why does it get a bad rap? Actually, it doesn't. All the sugar we consume in the form of sucrose and fructose does: everything packed into our foods and drinks to make them sweeter, more fun, and more addictive.

Fructose makes up half of table sugar, more than three-quarters of popular alternatives like agave syrup, and because it's cheap to manufacture, it's the sweetener of choice in soda, breakfast cereals, breads, and most of the processed foods bursting from the heart of our supermarkets.

Sugar has become the main source of calories in the American diet, with most of those calories coming from high-fructose corn syrup (HFCS), which is implicated in contributing to obesity, cardiovascular disease, diabetes, and non-alcoholic fatty liver disease.

Critics of the extensive use of HFCS in food sweetening argue that the highly processed substance is more harmful to humans than regular sugar, contributing to weight gain by affecting normal appetite functions.

Set aside HFCS for the moment: sucrose itself feeds obesity, tooth decay, diabetes, pancreatic damage, premature aging, osteoporosis, and hyperactivity in children. Sugar also contributes to intensifying heart disease and autoimmune diseases such as arthritis, asthma, and multiple sclerosis.

In 2012, Dr. Robert Lustig, one of the nation's best-known experts on obesity, addressing an audience at U.C. Berkeley, noted that fructose differs from glucose, sugar's other half.

As U.C. Berkeley News Center quotes Lustig, "Fructose has to be processed by the liver, like a cocktail. Glucose can be used directly by the body, which has a clever process for summoning insulin to help ferry the sugar to cells and to send hormonal signals when it needs energy or has had enough. Fructose, waiting its turn for processing in the liver, builds up in the blood and the body's clever messaging systems are disrupted. The result: People keep eating and don't feel like exercising; fat builds up in the wrong places; and insulin resistance, metabolic syndrome, Type 2 diabetes and obesity are inevitable."

Inevitable. And we're doing this damage to ourselves, by choice. The trend is mind-blowing:

In 1800, the average person ingested approximately 18 pounds of sugar per year. A hundred years later, in 1900, individual consumption had shot up to 90 pounds annually. The trend by 2009 saw more than half of America consuming a half pound of sugar per day, or more than 150 pounds of sugar per year.

Refined sugar is everywhere, addictive, and poisonous, and, as the American Medical Association attested in 2013 by naming obesity a medical condition and epidemic, there are consequences for all of us.

Let's drill down. Sugar is carbohydrate, composed of carbon, hydrogen, and oxygen. There are various types of sugar derived from different sources. Chemically different substances may also have a sweet taste but are not classified as sugars. Some are used as lower-calorie food substitutes for sugar described as artificial sweeteners.

From a metabolic point of view, refined sugars are completely stripped of all-natural healthy components such as vitamins and minerals. They consist of a simple carbohydrate that delivers zero health benefits. This incomplete carbohydrate metabolism forms harmful toxins in the body and high uric acid levels, which in turn interrupts the natural metabolic function and leads to the formation of degenerative diseases and a higher risk for heart disease.

It's easy to become overwhelmed with all of the different forms of sugars, including non-calorie sugar substitutes, but here's what you need to know about your market and dietary choices, both the bad and the good:

— Dextrose, fructose, and glucose are all monosaccharides, also known as simple sugars. The primary difference between them is in how your body metabolizes them. Dextrose is the primary term used on the ingredient list from food manufacturers.

— High-fructose corn syrup HFCS is a laboratory-made sugar consisting of 55 percent fructose and 45 percent glucose. This is probably the most dangerous form of sugar, as the entire burden on metabolizing HFCS falls with the liver, a process that results in permanent liver damage.

— Sugar alcohols such as xylitol, glycerol, sorbitol, maltitol, mannitol, and erythritol are neither sugars nor alcohols, but are becoming increasingly popular as sweeteners in mainstream "diet" products. They are incompletely digested in the intestine, so they provide fewer calories than sugar, but often cause problems with bloating, diarrhea, and flatulence.

— Sucralose is not a sugar, but rather a chlorinated artificial sweetener in line with aspartame and saccharin, with detrimental health effects to match. These bring increased risks for cancer, bone disease, and migraines, to name only a few.

— Honey in the raw is approximately 50 percent fructose, but it is completely natural in its raw form and has many health benefits when used in moderation, including a high antioxidant profile.

— Stevia is a highly sweet herb derived from the leaf of the South American stevia plant, which is completely safe in its natural form. Just like any supplement or food product, the integrity and quality of the product is essential for receiving the optimal health benefits.

The stevia plants used to make SweetLeaf® are grown South America, where the plant is native and has the best conditions for optimal growth and nutrient content. SweetLeaf® uses the entire stevia leaf, not just the sweetest part of the leaf like other stevia manufacturers. This process increases the nutrient value, and consumers have commented that they prefer the balanced taste compared to other products.

Furthermore, during the processing portion of SweetLeaf®, only purified water is used, unlike other manufacturers, which use chemicals such as methanol or ethanol. Instead of using nutrient-free fillers such as sugar, SweetLeaf® stevia is blended with inulin, the fibrous extract from the chickaree root, which itself has numerous health benefits.

Our conclusion? Using SweetLeaf® 100 percent natural stevia sweetener in moderation is a safe way to start eliminating sugars, HFCS, and artificial sweeteners from your diet, and live healthfully, happily, and longer … truly the sweet life.

References

Sugar: UCSF's Lustig on why we love it, and how it's killing us. Retrieved from newscenter.berkeley. edu/2012/05/04/robert-lustig-the-guy-on-obesity-speaking-may-3

Johnson, R.J. and Gower, T. (2009). The Sugar Fix: The High-Fructose Fallout That is Making You Sick and Fat, New York: Rodale Inc.

Naked Food Cooking. What is the Best Sweetener? Retrieved from www.nakedfoodcooking.com/best-sweetener

Stanhope, Kimber L., et al. "Consuming fructose-sweetened, not glucose-sweetened,beverages increases visceral adiposity and lipids and decreases insulin sensitivity in overweight/obese humans." The Journal of Clinical Investigation 119(5) (2009): 1322-1334.

SweetLeaf® Stevia Sweetener. Retrieved from www. sweetleaf.com

Vacuum Sealing, Blast Freezing Mean Safer, Healthier Food

DANA YARN, R.D., L.D., AND
DR. KEITH KANTOR, N.D., PH.D.

S AMERICA'S FOOD SUPPLY SAFE? DOES IT SUSTAIN US and keep us healthy? When we examine the growing industrialized food industry, and study how most of our country's food is grown, manufactured, processed, packaged, shipped, stored, marketed, and consumed, the answer is clearly no.

The food industry is extremely productive, but the producers have their eye on efficiency and profit. Consumers' health and well-being — what food is supposed to provide — ranks a distant third in consideration. Foods that are stripped of nutrients, bathed in ammonia, bleached, stabilized, preserved, genetically modified, standardized, and left to sit in sometimes toxic packaging do us no favors.

Indeed, food industrialization is directly related to a steady increase in food recalls and food-borne illness. The bacterium *E. coli* sickens roughly 73,000 Americans each year, with an overall 76 million cases of food-borne illnesses befalling Americans annually. Many cases go unreported.

The average American isn't aware the human body quickly becomes addicted to foods containing excess sodium, sugar, and saturated and trans fats. That these ingredients feature so prominently in processed and fast foods (which consist also of a fair amount of filler) help explain our country's obesity epidemic; our increase of heart disease, diabetes, and cancer; and the nation's overall — and economically crippling — health care costs.

Consider recombinant bovine growth hormone (rBGH), a synthetic hormone marketed to dairy farmers to increase cows' milk production. It's been used in the United States since 1993, when the Food and Drug Administration approved it, but it's not permitted in the European Union, Canada, and other countries, which do not suffer as many related maladies as we do in the U.S.

In the United States, at least, the Natural Products Association says livestock on farms certified USDA All-natural shall not be given unnecessary antibiotics or growth hormones, in contrast to common practice in conventional agriculture. These treatments are banned in Australia, Canada, Japan, New Zealand, and all 25 nations of the European Union over concern of their effects on humans.

Look at what's happening with conventional beef cattle, poultry, and swine: they're fed antimicrobials routinely for non-therapeutic purposes. Experts show that antibiotics in the food supply contribute to the excessive rise of antibiotic resistance and so-called superbugs.

Then there are food labels, marketing, and advertising campaigns touting "free-range" and "hormone-free" foods. Don't be misled. Those labels aren't equal to the far superior designation "USDA All-natural," which assures that the food is grown, harvested, and processed according to rigorous U.S. Department of Agriculture standards that include restrictions on amounts and residues of pesticides, hormones, and antibiotics. Foods labeled USDA All-natural cannot have been treated with any sewage sludge, bioengineering, or ionizing radiation.

The benefits of eating USDA All-natural foods include higher nutrient values, tastier food, and demonstrably — and dramatically — environmentally friendly manufacturing. The nutrient content of our America's food supply has decreased 1,000 percent in the past 60 years, during which time more than 70,000 new chemicals have been introduced to our foods. Only time will tell what impact these foods will have on our bodies and national economy.

USDA All-natural food for your health

Food is for fueling us, sustaining our intricate and wonderful biology, and preventing and managing disease.

That's it. That's why we eat and drink. There's no job or room for chemicals, additives, dyes, steroids, hormones, and antibiotics, simply because those additions and subtractions don't fit with what we're built to run on. They're a burden to us, and our bodies struggle to cope with them until they can't, and that's why we have so many expensive, debilitating, and deadly diseases.

If the food you buy at the market, or order at restaurants, isn't labeled "USDA All-natural," you're eating what a corporate accountant decided was the least expensive, only marginally nutritious product the producer needed to ship to keep the greatest profit margin.

In contrast, "USDA All-natural" is a guarantee of nutritious food for you and your family.

Lack of food inspections

Another threat to our national food safety: lack of food inspections. Imports account for nearly 60 percent of the fruits and vegetables, and 75 percent of the seafood that we consume; yet only 1 percent of those foods are inspected as they cross our borders.

Dean Wyatt, a USDA veterinarian who oversees federal slaughterhouse inspectors, says his agency regularly punishes inspectors for writing up legitimate safety violations:

"Hundreds of scientists and inspectors responsible for food safety have personally experienced political interference in their work, and that's bad for public health. Upper-level management does not adequately support field inspectors and the actions they take to protect the food supply," said Wyatt.

Francesca Grifo, director of the Union of Concerned Scientists' Scientific Integrity Program, agrees: "Not only is there lack of support, but there's outright obstruction, retaliation and abuse of power," Grifo said.

In contrast, 100 percent of foods procured and distributed by Green Box Foods is inspected daily by the USDA to ensure the safety and quality of all its products.

The hidden toll on our environment

Pesticides. Despite natural food's rising popularity, the United States relies principally on a farming system that uses roughly a half-million tons of toxic pesticides annually, which extracts and burn millions of gallons of fossil fuels while polluting our waterways and blood streams.

Waste. Each year, 817 million tons of food is shipped around the planet, resulting in a basic diet of imported products using four times the energy, and producing four times the emissions, of an equivalent domestic diet.

Why waste so much energy? Buy your food from local producers. This avoids long-distance travel and overuse of plastic packaging and chemical preservatives required for transporting food long distances.

The benefits of flash freezing and vacuum sealing

Green Box Foods, a respected leader in entrepreneurial, environmental, and food industry innovation, helps its customers lower their impact on the environment and live better in the process. Our flash-frozen, chemical-free meats, fish, and vegetables are packaged in a material called DuPont Iolon film, which is completely biodegradable. By flash freezing and vacuum sealing, we kill essentially all bacteria and prevent cross contamination.

When any meat is vacuum-sealed within an impermeable polymer, oxygen can't get inside the package or reach the product. This lack of oxygen kills all the aerobic bacteria (bacteria that need oxygen to live).

By killing aerobic bacteria, such as salmonella, the product is cleaner and safer. This also causes the meat to appear darker (purplish red) versus the bright red you'll see stacked in your supermarket meat aisle.

By blast freezing the product at 50 degrees below zero, several things occur:

— We lock flavors into the product.

— There's no crystallization on or in the product, making for more consistent preparation and plating, as the food's fibrous stromal proteins are left unbroken.

— The process kills 99.47 percent of anaerobic bacteria such as *E. coli* — instantly.

Under the microscope

Flash freezing and vacuum sealing are simply cleaner and safer than the conventional status quo, and you should buy these foods to avoid the problems you'll get with the conventional status quo. If you were to drill down microscopically, you would see how it works: muscle tissue contains many proteins that serve many different functions. These proteins are grouped into three general classifications: myofibrilar, sarcoplasmic, and stromal.

Myofibrilar proteins are also known as salt-soluble proteins because of their ability to be dissolved in salt solutions. The sarcoplasmic proteins consist mainly of the glycolytic enzymes. These proteins are also known as the water-soluble proteins.

Myoglobin, the oxygen-binding protein inside the muscle cell and hemoglobin, are members of this protein class. Myoglobin and hemoglobin are responsible for meat's typical red color. The darker color of beef compared to pork (or chicken leg vs. chicken breast muscle) is due to larger quantities of these pigment proteins. The heme group also changes in color with oxygen binding and oxidation and when complexed with nitrite during meat curing. Stromal proteins, or connective tissue proteins, consist primarily of collagen and elastin.

In order to get the bright red color, which is usually seen on the surface of meat you'll find in the supermarket, oxygen from the air needs to react with the meat pigments or sarcoplasmic proteins. When oxygen attaches itself to the myoglobin, it is converted to oxymyoglobin, the pigment responsible for the red color in meat.

Sure, that bright red color is appealing, but the oxygen responsible for it also degrades the meat and leaves it susceptible to aerobic bacteria. For instance, growth of psychrophilic bacteria (spoilage bacteria) is sustained because of high oxygen transmission rates through materials used for meat packages in the supermarket.

Most of the problems addressed with tray and over-wrap packaging of fresh or frozen meat are perfectly overcome with vacuum packaging. If more consumers understood how oxygen affects their uncooked meat — and their meal to come — they would clearly insist on vacuum packaging. Composite polymer films, also known as laminates, have low water vapor and oxygen transmission rates and are used for vacuum packaging.

In vacuum packaging, metmyoglobin is formed because of low levels of oxygen that are trapped in superficial tissue layers. However, basically all pigment forms transform gradually to the purplish-red deoxymyoglin, as respiratory enzymes in muscle and microorganisms use the leftover oxygen. Carbon dioxide formation and some pH lowering from carbonic acid formation results from this respiratory activity.

For vacuum-packaged ground beef, or any meat, a purplish-red color is common as the vacuum condition prevents air from making contact with the ground beef. Vacuum packaging, combined with an oxygen-impermeable film, could dramatically improve shelf life of all meats. Blast freezing naturally improves shelf life from there.

So look for USDA All-natural, locally sourced foods, and check to make sure they're protected by vacuum sealing and blast freezing. When you do, what's served at your place of employment, your favorite restaurant, and your kitchen table will feed you well, for life.

References

American Association of Meat Processors, October 2010.

Water: The Most Overlooked Nutrient

DANA YARN, R.D., L.D., AND
DR. KEITH KANTOR, N.D., PH.D.

WATER? A NUTRIENT? ABSOLUTELY, AND A vital one.

When we talk about nutrition and health, we usually talk about counting calories, eating less sugar and harmful fats, and consuming more fiber. But quite often we overlook the benefits of getting enough water. Drinking an adequate amount of water is not just a good thing you should do; it's a good thing you should do for very specific reasons.

Our bodies are composed of more than 60 percent water. This essential nutrient keeps our body in a state of balance and provides us with energy and other nutrients. The functions of these bodily fluids, primarily water, include digestion, absorption, circulation, creation of saliva, transportation of nutrients, and maintenance of body temperature.

According to H.H. Mitchell in the *Journal of Biological Chemistry*, the brain and heart are composed of 73 percent water, and the lungs are about 83 percent water. The skin contains 64 percent water, with the muscles and kidneys sloshing in at 79 percent water. Even the bones are watery, at 31 percent.

And interestingly, Mitchell reports, people with more fatty tissue have less water than people with less fatty tissue, as a percentage.

We do take in water from what we eat and drink. But we lose fluid continuously from skin evaporation, breathing, urine, and stool, and we must replace these losses daily for good health.

When your water intake falls below your output, you can become dehydrated. Fluid losses are accentuated in warmer climates, during strenuous exercise, in high altitudes, and in older adults, whose sense of thirst may not be as sharp as when they were younger.

Water intake guidelines

Here's how much is enough: aim to take in about half of your body weight in ounces of water per day. Generally, a man needs about three liters per day, while a woman needs about two and a quarter liters per day. Pregnant and nursing women need more.

Children need between five and eight cups of water each day, according to a study led by researchers at Queens College of the City University of New York and published in the October 2010 issue of the *American Journal of Clinical Nutrition*.

Kids in sporting events are particularly susceptible to dehydration. The Texas EDEN Disaster Resources Database recommends kids drink at least 12 fluid ounces two to three hours before a sporting event. Aim for 12 to

20 fluid ounces. (Kids who sweat excessively should drink more, EDEN says.) No child on the field should go longer than 15 minutes without drinking water, and all should rehydrate after the game or practice ends. If the activity goes longer than an hour, rehydrate with something that restores electrolytes.

Water helps with weight loss

If your goal is optimal health and weight loss, plain water is the best option. You can add flavorful, fresh-cut fruit to your water without adding too many calories. Lemon, lime, berries, or melon are all are great in plain water. This is guaranteed not to drive up insulin levels, as flavored coffee drinks, juices, sweet teas, and sodas certainly do.

Keeping insulin levels under control allows the body to burn fat rather than store it. Warning: Artificially sweetened diet drinks have been shown to alter blood sugar levels and increase the risk of certain cancers and thyroid disruption that goes along with consuming artificial sweeteners. For the best results, stick with plain water.

Often the early sign of hunger is thirst or dehydration. When you ignore thirst, you might wind up taking on extra — and excessive — calories. Try drinking one to two cups of water before each meal. You'll take on significantly fewer calories, so that's an easy way to keep the pounds off.

Water means energy

Water provides our muscles with energy. When muscle cells fail to maintain their balance of fluids and electrolytes they shrivel, which can result in muscle fatigue and poor performance. Simply put, when muscles lack the right amount of water, they weaken. Our energy and performance suffer. This is especially true for those who play sports or who work outside in hot climates.

Keep it clean

Our kidneys do an amazing job of filtering toxins from our blood stream, just so long our daily intake of water keeps up. Body fluids, which are principally water, meet an amazing variety of jobs for us. Importantly, water helps transport waste products out of our cells. The body's main toxin is blood urea nitrogen, a water-soluble waste that passes through the kidneys to be excreted in the urine. When we get enough fluids, urine flows freely, is light in color, and free of odor. When we don't get enough fluids, urine concentration, color, and odor increase as the kidneys trap extra fluid for bodily functions.

Over time, if you chronically drink a low amount of fluids, you might be at higher risk for kidney stones and gouty arthritis, especially during the hot months.

Water for health

Some tips to increase your fluid intake and increase your overall health through the benefits of water:

• Drink one or two cups of water before every snack and meal, but avoid drinking a lot while eating, as this could dilute digestive enzymes, leading to an upset stomach and bloating.

• Bored with plain water? Add fresh fruit to it and let it sit in a glass pitcher overnight to fully infuse with the flavor of the fruit. You're likely to drink more liquids if you like the way they taste.

• Eat more fruits and vegetables. Their high water content will add to your hydration. About 20 percent of our fluid intake comes from foods.

• Keep a container of water with you in your car, at your desk, and in your bag. It's best to drink out of BPA (Bisphenol A)-free containers such as glass and stainless steel.

• Drink filtered water when possible. The preferred filtration system is reverse osmosis, which has been proven to remove the most toxins, including lead, excessive sodium, and parasites. These toxins could disrupt your metabolism, including thyroid and sex hormone balance. Moreover contaminated water could compromise children's developing immune systems, as well as those of the elderly and anyone suffering with an autoimmune disorder or undergoing treatment for cancer.

When it comes to water and overall health, you have a world of options. Dive in.

References

CDC; Lead and Drinking Water from Private Wells; May 2010. http://www.cdc.gov/healthywater/drinking/private/wells/disease/lead.html

Recipes *for* Good Health

How to supercharge your superheroes? Serve or order them all the good stuff, encourage them to cut out the bad stuff, and teach them that they'll get out of life what they put into it. (The same goes for grown-ups, incidentally.) Here's your family's quick-start guide to breakfast, lunch, and dinner the Green Box Foods way. Make it your way, too — and don't forget to drink plenty of water and get plenty of super-heroic sleep.

Breakfast

ADAM APPLE FRENCH TOAST

Makes 2 servings

Ingredients

1 teaspoon of organic butter or coconut oil

1 large apple (organic Granny Smith or Red Delicious), cored and diced

4 ounces all-natural apple juice (avoid the kind with high-fructose corn syrup)

2 ounces raw, local honey

4 slices of gluten-free day-old bread

2 large eggs, cage-free if possible

4 ounces of egg whites

¼ cup unsweetened almond, coconut, or rice milk

Dash pure vanilla extract

Pinch cinnamon

Pinch nutmeg

Directions

- Step 1. Coat the inside of a small skillet with 1 teaspoon of organic butter or coconut oil; heat to medium high

- Step 2. Add the diced apple and sauté for 2 minutes; add the apple juice and honey; reduce heat to keep warm

- Step 3. In a bowl, mix the egg whites, milk, whole eggs, vanilla, nutmeg, and cinnamon

- Step 4. Heat a large, nonstick-sprayed skillet

- Step 5. Dip the bread slices into egg mix and fry on medium high; flip when browned; serve two per plate, top with apple mixture

BERRY MUFFINS

Makes 12 muffins

Ingredients

2 cups amaranth (or other gluten-free) flour

⅔ cups raw sugar or raw local honey

½ teaspoon baking powder, aluminum-free

½ teaspoon baking soda

¼ teaspoon sea salt or Himalayan salt

¼ cup fresh or frozen blueberries, organic if possible

¼ cup sliced strawberries, fresh or frozen, and organic if possible

¼ cup raspberries, fresh or frozen, and organic if possible

¾ cup of full-fat buttermilk, organic if possible

3 tablespoons melted butter, organic (and from grass-fed cows if possible)

1 large egg, cage-free, beaten

Directions

- Step 1. Preheat oven to 350 degrees

- Step 2. In a large bowl, sift together all dry ingredients

- Step 3. In a separate bowl, mix the buttermilk, egg, melted butter, and fruit

- Step 4. With a rubber spatula, gently fold the egg/fruit mixture into dry ingredients

- Step 5. Place paper muffin cups in tin, and evenly spoon mixture into tin

- Step 6. Bake for 20 to 22 minutes or until golden brown

- Step 7. Remove from tin and cool on wire rack; serve

BIANCA BROCCOLI QUICHE

Serves 4

Ingredients

1 teaspoon of organic butter or coconut oil

1 cup broccoli florets

4 ounces minced onion

2 large eggs, beaten

4 ounces egg whites

¼ cup unsweetened almond, coconut, or rice milk

½ cup full-fat shredded cheddar cheese, organic if possible

Sea salt or Himalayan salt and pepper to taste

<u>Gluten-Free Pie Crust</u>

2 cups blanched almond flour

½ teaspoon sea salt or Himalayan salt

2 tablespoons melted coconut oil or butter

1 egg

Place flour and salt in food processor and pulse briefly

Add coconut oil and egg and pulse until mixture forms a ball

Press dough into a 9-inch metal tart pan

Place pie filling of your choice in crust

Bake pie as directed per pie recipe

Directions
- Step 1. Preheat oven to 325 degrees
- Step 2. In a medium skillet coated with 1 teaspoon organic butter or coconut oil, cook onion on medium high until tender
- Step 3. Add broccoli, salt, and pepper to taste; cook until tender; remove from heat
- Step 4. Mix eggs, egg whites, and milk.
- Step 5. Spread ¼ cup of cheese on bottom of pie crust; add broccoli and onion mix; add egg mix; top with remaining cheese
- Step 6. Bake for 30 minutes or until egg mix is firm and cheese is browned; remove and cut into four wedges

CANADIAN GRITS

Serves 6

Ingredients

1 teaspoon of organic butter or coconut oil

4 ½ cups water

1 cup gluten-free yellow corn grits

¼ teaspoon sea salt

1 clove minced garlic

½ cup diced onion

½ cup diced nitrate-free Canadian bacon

½ cup sharp shredded white cheddar cheese

Directions
- Step 1. Preheat oven to 325 degrees
- Step 2. In large saucepan, bring water to boil, add salt and grits, stirring occasionally; reduce heat to simmer; cook until grits thicken
- Step 3. Coat small skillet with 1 teaspoon organic butter or coconut oil; heat to medium high; add onion; cook until browned
- Step 4. Add garlic and Canadian bacon; cook until hot, and keep warm
- Step 5. Coat an 8-inch (round or square) Pyrex dish; add grits and top with onion bacon mix; top with cheddar cheese
- Step 6. Bake uncovered until cheese browns; serve

VERY BERRY SMOOTHIE

Makes two 16-ounce servings

Ingredients

2 cups fresh or frozen berries, washed: e.g., strawberries, raspberries, blueberries

2 cups full-fat Greek yogurt (plain)

2 cups unsweetened almond, coconut, or rice milk

3-5 ice cubes (optional)

Directions
- Step 1. Add berries, yogurt, milk, and ice to blender
- Step 2. Blend on high until thoroughly mixed; serve cold

211

VERY BERRY CRISP

Makes six servings

Ingredients

2 cups fresh or frozen organic blueberries, washed and thawed

2 cups fresh or frozen organic raspberries, washed and thawed

2 cups sliced fresh or frozen organic strawberries, washed and thawed

⅓ cup almond or coconut flour

1 cup regular, old-fashioned, gluten-free oats

1 teaspoon cinnamon

½ cup brown sugar or raw honey, local if possible

¼ cup melted coconut oil or organic butter

Directions

- Step 1. Preheat oven to 350 degrees
- Step 2. Lightly coat an 8-inch by 8-inch Pyrex dish with organic butter or coconut oil
- Step 3. Mix fruits in a medium bowl
- Step 4. In a separate bowl, mix flour, oats, sugar, cinnamon, and oil
- Step 5. Place fruit in Pyrex dish; cover evenly in oat mixture
- Step 6. Bake for 30 minutes or until top is brown and bubbly; serve hot

VEGGIE SKILLET FRITTATA

Serves 4

Ingredients

1 teaspoon of organic butter or coconut oil

1 cup egg whites

1 cup whole eggs, beaten

6 ounces spinach, fresh or frozen

2 ounces tomatoes, diced

2 ounces onion, diced

2 ounces roasted red pepper, diced

4 ounces nitrate-free turkey sausage, cooked and diced

½ cup shredded full-fat cheddar cheese, organic, if possible

Sea salt or Himalayan salt and pepper to taste

Directions

- Step 1. In a large skillet coated with organic butter or coconut oil, and heated to medium high, sauté spinach, onion, tomato, turkey sausage, and red pepper until soft
- Step 2. Add eggs; with a high-heat rubber spatula, pull egg/vegetable sausage mix from sides of pan towards center of pan, until mix appears cooked
- Step 3. Season to taste; add cheese; lower heat to warm; keep covered for 5 minutes
- Step 4. Cut into four wedges; serve hot

VEGETARIAN EGGS BENEDICT

Serves 2

Ingredients

1 teaspoon of organic butter or coconut oil

2 large portabella mushrooms, cleaned (stem removed, gills scraped off)

2 ounces roasted red pepper, diced

2 ounces onion, minced

4 ounces fresh or frozen spinach

2 ounces artichoke hearts, diced

1 clove garlic, minced

4 whole eggs

Directions

• Step 1. Roast mushrooms in 350-degree oven for 5 minutes; cool, drain, then pat dry with paper towel

• Step 2. Coat large skillet with 1 teaspoon organic butter or coconut oil; sauté pepper, onion, spinach, artichoke, and garlic

• Step 3. On baking sheet, arrange mushrooms tops down; add vegetable mix; bake at 250 degrees for 5 minutes

• Step 4. Cook eggs in your desired style: over easy, etc.

• Step 5. Top mushrooms with eggs; serve hot

TURKEY HASH

Serves 2

Ingredients

1 teaspoon of organic butter or coconut oil

½ pound ground turkey

4 ounces minced onion

4 ounces fine diced cooked Idaho potatoes

2 ounces minced green bell pepper

4 ounces half egg whites and half whole egg

2 ounces ketchup (avoid the kind with high-fructose corn syrup)

1 teaspoon sea salt or Himalayan salt

½ teaspoon ground black pepper

Directions

• Step 1. Combine all ingredients; heat large skillet to medium high; coat with 1 teaspoon organic butter or coconut oil

• Step 2. Add hash mix to pan; cook for 3 minutes; turn and repeat

• Step 3. Cook until internal temperature reaches 165 degrees

• Step 4. Top with your favorite egg style: poached, scrambled, etc.

VACATION CAR COOLER BREAKFAST

Serves 1

Ingredients

4 ounces full-fat Greek yogurt, plain

1 ripe banana or mixed berries

4 ounces granola or trail mix

Directions

• Step 1. In 8-ounce cup with lid, layer granola mix, fruit, yogurt; repeat as needed

• Step 2. Store in cooler; serve cold

SUPER-STAR SCRAMBLER

Serves 4

Ingredients

1 teaspoon of organic butter or coconut oil

8-ounce mixture ½ egg whites and ½ whole eggs (cage-free)

1 ounce roasted red pepper, diced

1 ounce onion, minced

1 ounce asparagus, diced

6 ounces fresh spinach

1 ounce broccoli florets

1 ounce tomato, diced

1 ounce mushroom, sliced

1 ounce artichoke hearts, sliced

4 ounces pepper jack cheese, sliced

Directions

• Step 1. Coat large skillet with 1 teaspoon organic butter or coconut oil; heat to medium high

• Step 2. Add onions, cook for 2 minutes, and add remaining ingredients except egg mixture and cheese; cook until tender

• Step 3. Add egg mixture; stir constantly until cooked thoroughly

• Step 4. Add cheese; serve hot

STUFFED BREAKFAST POTATO

Serves 2

Ingredients

1 teaspoon of organic butter or coconut oil

1 large baked potato, cooled

1 ounce diced onion

1 ounce diced green pepper

2 ounce diced cooked nitrate-free turkey or regular bacon

2 ounces full-fat shredded cheddar cheese, organic, if possible

1 egg

Salt and pepper to taste

Directions

• Step 1. Preheat oven to 350 degrees

• Step 2. Cut cooled potato in half lengthwise

• Step 3. Carefully spoon out potato, leaving skin intact

• Step 4. In small sauté pan, add 1 teaspoon organic butter or coconut oil; heat to medium high; cook onion and pepper until tender; let cool

• Step 5. Dice potato, mix with pepper, onion, bacon, egg, salt, and pepper; fill potato shell with mixture; top with cheese and bake until cheese is browned and internal temperature reaches 145 degrees

STRAWBERRY OATMEAL FOREVER

Serves 1

Ingredients

½ cup cooked (approx. ¼ cup dry) steel-cut or old-fashioned gluten-free oats

½ cup unsweetened coconut, almond, or rice milk

1 tablespoon all-natural strawberry preserves (avoid the kind with high-fructose corn syrup)

½ cup washed, cleaned, sliced strawberries, organic if possible

Directions

• Step 1. In small saucepan, heat milk on medium high until hot

• Step 2. Mix in strawberry preserves; reduce heat

• Step 3. Prepare oatmeal as directed on container; put in small bowl

• Step 4. Top with milk/strawberry combination; top with sliced strawberries; serve hot

NUT BUTTER/BACON/ BANANA SANDWICH

Serves 1

Ingredients

2 slices gluten-free bread, toasted

2 slices cooked nitrate-free turkey or regular bacon

4 ounces natural almond, cashew, or peanut butter

½ ripe banana, sliced

Directions

• Step 1. Spread nut butter evenly on both side of toasted bread

• Step 2. Add bacon

• Step 3. Add banana

• Step 4. Close sandwich, cut in half

NUTTY ORANGE/ CRANBERRY PANCAKES

Makes 6 portions

Ingredients

1 teaspoon of organic butter or coconut oil

½ cup gluten-free oat flour

½ cup ground flax seed

¼ cup amaranth gluten-free flour

⅓ cup raw sugar or local raw honey

1 teaspoon baking soda

1 teaspoon baking powder (aluminum free)

½ teaspoon sea salt or Himalayan salt

1 ½ cups unsweet almond, coconut, or rice milk

1 large egg, beaten

¼ cup orange marmalade (avoid the kind with high-fructose corn syrup)

½ cup cranberry sauce (avoid the kind with high-fructose corn syrup)

½ cup toasted almonds

¼ cup pure maple syrup (avoid the kind with high-fructose corn syrup)

Directions

• Step 1. Sift together all dry ingredients mix except almonds

• Step 2. Mix egg, milk, and honey

• Step 3. With rubber spatula, fold liquid ingredients into dry ingredients until mixed throughly

• Step 4. Coat large skillet with 1 teaspoon of organic butter or coconut oil; heat to medium high

• Step 5. Spoon 2 ounces batter each into pan; cook until top bubbles; flip; cook until other side is golden brown; keep warm

• Step 6. Combine orange marmalade and cranberry sauce; heat over low heat until hot

• Step 7. Spoon over pancakes; top with almonds and maple syrup

HILLARY HONEYDEW'S BEACH BLANKET BREAKFAST

Serves 4

Ingredients

1 large, ripe honeydew melon

1 pint ripe strawberries, organic if possible

1 bunch red or green grapes, organic if possible, washed and picked

8-ounce can pineapple, diced and drained

4-ounce can mandarin oranges, drained

Directions

- Step 1. Cut honeydew in a cross cut/jagged cut pattern from center of melon

- Step 2. Scoop out seeds, then with melon baller scoop out flesh of melon. (Scoop as close to skin as possible without scooping rind.) Put in container

- Step 3. Remove strawberry caps; wash and slice strawberries, add to melon ball mix

- Step 4. Add grapes, pineapple, and mandarin orange to mix

- Step 5. Refrigerate honeydew shell in large container or put in cooler with fruit mix

- Step 6. Separate melon, add fruit mix, and serve chilled

HEALTHY HUEVOS RANCHEROS

Makes 4 servings

Ingredients

1 teaspoon of organic butter or coconut oil

4 6-inch gluten-free tortillas

8 ounces cooked nitrate-free turkey or regular bacon (diced)

2 large, ripe tomatoes, seeded and diced

1 medium green pepper, seeded and diced

1 large onion, diced

16 ounces half egg whites and half whole eggs

1 ounce dried cumin

1 ounce dried chili powder

1 ounce sea salt or Himalayan salt

1 ounce ground black pepper

Dash of cayenne pepper

½ cup full-fat shredded cheddar cheese (organic, if possible)

Directions

- Step 1. Preheat oven to 325 degrees

- Step 2. Coat skillet with organic butter or coconut oil

- Step 3. Sauté onion, pepper, tomato, and spices until tender,

- Step 4. Heat small pan (coated with coconut oil or butter) to medium high

- Step 5. Cook egg mixture 4 ounces at a time; flip once until cooked

- Step 6. On nonstick sheet pan, add tortillas; top each with egg mixture; divide vegetable mix evenly; sprinkle with cheddar cheese

- Step 7. Bake for 3 minutes or until cheese is melted

- Step 8. Top with turkey or bacon; serve hot

GREEN TEAM OMELET

Makes 1 serving

Ingredients

2 ounces steamed broccoli, chopped and cooled

2 ounces steamed asparagus, chopped and cooled

4 ounces steamed spinach, cooled

6 ounces blend of half egg whites, half whole eggs

1 teaspoon of organic butter or coconut oil

Sea salt or Himalayan salt

Pepper to taste

Directions

• Step 1. Heat sauté pan on medium heat, and coat with the butter or coconut oil

• Step 2. Add egg mixture

• Step 3. With a heat-resistant spatula, pull eggs from side of pan toward center until dry

• Step 4. Flip eggs over; add vegetables; fold eggs over to cover

• Step 5. Season to taste, then serve hot

EGGS ARNOLD (BENEDICT)

Makes 1 portion

Ingredients

3 cups cold water

2 small whole eggs, cage free

4 ounces spinach, steamed (fresh or frozen spinach)

2 slices tomato

1 gluten-free English muffin

1 ounce sour cream, all-natural full-fat

1 ounce olive-oil-based mayonnaise

1 teaspoon lemon juice

2 teaspoons chopped chive

Pinch of cayenne pepper

Directions

• Step 1. Pour 3 cups cold water in small saucepan, and heat to boiling

• Step 2. Toast muffin to desired brownness

• Step 3. Combine sour cream, mayonnaise, lemon juice, and cayenne pepper

• Step 4. Crack open eggs, add to boiling water, and cook until desired doneness

• Step 5. Plate two muffin halves, 1 slice tomato each, and add spinach to each

• Step 6. Place one egg on each; top with sour cream/ mayo mixture

• Step 7. Sprinkle with chives; serve hot

Lunch

ASIAN TERIYAKI BEEF SIZZLING SALAD

Serves 4

Ingredients

1 pound flank steak (fat and silver skin trimmed)

2 ounces onion, sliced

2 ounces sliced green bell pepper

2 ounces water chestnuts

2 ounces broccoli florets

2 ounces baby corn

2 ounces sliced mushrooms

2 cloves minced garlic

1 ounce fresh-minced ginger

24 ounces chopped romaine lettuce

6 ounces reduced-sodium teriyaki sauce (avoid the kind with MSG added, if possible)

2 ounces rice wine vinegar

1 ounce cornstarch

1 teaspoon minced scallion

1 ounce bean sprouts

2 teaspoons coconut oil or organic butter

2 teaspoons sesame oil

Directions

•   Step 1. Marinate steak with 3 ounces teriyaki sauce and 1 ounce rice wine vinegar; refrigerate overnight

•   Step 2. Thin-slice steak against the grain

•   Step 3. Discard the marinade. In a large skillet, heated to medium high, add steak and cook briefly. Stir in coconut oil or butter, sesame oil, onion, pepper, broccoli, water chestnuts, baby corn, mushroom, garlic, and ginger

•   Step 4. Mix cornstarch in with remaining teriyaki and rice wine vinegar; add to skillet and heat until thickened, then remove

•   Step 5. Divide lettuce into four large salad bowls; top with meat and vegetable mix; garnish with bean sprouts and scallion

MULTICOLORED CORN SALAD

Great as a side for lunch or dinner

Ingredients

2 cups frozen corn, thawed

3 cups canned black beans, drained and rinsed

1 large onion, diced (organic, if possible)

1 green bell pepper, seeded and diced (organic, if possible)

1 red bell pepper, seeded and diced (organic, if possible)

2 ribs (stalks) celery, diced (organic, if possible)

2 cloves minced garlic

2 tablespoons fresh oregano, chopped

2 tablespoons fresh parsley, chopped

2 tablespoons fresh basil, chopped

½ cup olive oil

¼ cup red wine vinegar

Salt and ground black pepper to taste

Directions

•   Step 1. In a large bowl, combine the corn, beans, onion, green and red pepper, and celery

•   Step 2. In a small bowl, mix garlic, oregano, parsley, basil, salt, pepper, and red wine vinegar; whisk in olive oil until contents thicken

•   Step 3. Toss dressing with vegetables

•   Step 4. Refrigerate for 2 hours; serve cold

TURKEY BLT WRAP

Serves 1

Ingredients

4 ounces turkey, oven-roasted or deli-sliced nitrate-free/low-sodium

2 strips turkey bacon, nitrate-free or regular, cooked

3 ounces iceberg lettuce

3 slices medium tomato (organic, if possible)

2 ounces olive-oil-based mayonnaise

An 8-inch gluten-free wrap

Directions

• Step 1. Lay wrap down; spread mayonnaise three quarters of the way across

• Step 2. Place half lettuce down; put turkey on top, then put down turkey, bacon, tomato, and remaining lettuce.

• Step 3. Fold in sides of wrap, then roll bottom up to top until compact and complete

• Step 4. Cut in half; serve with pickle spear and choice of side

TUNA-STUFFED TOMATOES

Serves 1

Ingredients

1-4 ounce piece of fresh tuna

1 large beefsteak or other large tomato cut in half (spoon out flesh without damaging skin; reserve filling)

8 ounce spring-mix lettuce (organic, if possible)

2 ounces diced cucumber (organic, if possible)

2 ounces diced onion (organic, if possible)

2 ounces fresh lemon juice

1 ounce olive oil

½ teaspoon each garlic powder and paprika

Directions

• Step 1. Preheat grill or sauté pan

• Step 2. Coat tuna with olive oil, lemon juice, and spices

• Step 3. Grill or sauté tuna until it reaches 140 degrees

• Step 4. Put spring mix in salad bowl; top with cucumber, onion, and tomato reserve

• Step 5. Fill tomato with the cooled diced tuna; place tomato on salad topped with the dressing of your choice

SPICY AVOCADO SANDWICH SPREAD

Makes 2 cups
Perfect as spread for sandwiches, salad dressing, topping for entrees, and more

Ingredients

2 large ripe Haas avocados, halved, seed removed, peeled, finely diced, and tossed with 1 tablespoon of fresh lime juice

1 small onion, finely diced (organic, if possible)

2 ribs (stalks) of celery, finely diced (organic, if possible)

1 large cucumber, peeled, seeded, and finely diced

Clove garlic, finely diced

2 tablespoons Italian parsley, finely diced

1½ cup of olive oil-based mayonnaise

1 teaspoon Tabasco sauce

Salt and fresh ground pepper to taste

Directions

• Mix ingredients and refrigerate

APPLE CRANBERRY CABBAGE COLESLAW

Use as side dish for lunches, dinners, etc.

Ingredients

1 small head cabbage, green or Savoy, trimmed, halved, and cored, and thinly sliced

1 large Granny Smith apple, peeled, cored, and thinly sliced (organic, if possible)

¼ cup fresh lemon juice

¼ fresh parsley, chopped

½ cup olive-oil-based mayonnaise

½ cup plain full-fat Greek yogurt

1 teaspoon celery seed

¼ cup cranberry sauce

1 small onion, thinly sliced

Fresh pepper, ground to taste

Directions

• Step 1. In a large mixing bowl, add apple with lemon juice, cabbage, onion, parsley, and black pepper

• Step 2. In separate bowl, mix mayo, yogurt, celery seed, and cranberry sauce

• Step 3. Mix sauce with cabbage mix

• Step 4. Cover and refrigerate for 4 hours or overnight. Serve cold

SOUTHWEST TURKEY BURGER

Serves 1

Ingredients

4 ounces ground turkey

1 ounce diced jalapenos (organic, if possible)

1 ounce diced onion (organic, if possible)

1 ounce diced green pepper (organic, if possible)

1 ounce diced tomato

Garlic clove, minced

½ teaspoon ground cumin

½ teaspoon chili powder

Dash of cayenne pepper

½ avocado, diced (remove from skin and remove pit)

2 ounces lime juice

Salt and pepper to taste

Directions

• Step 1. Add lime juice to diced avocado

• Step 2. Combine with the other diced vegetables

• Step 3. Form ground turkey into a patty; cook in a nonstick-sprayed pan, heated to medium high

• Step 4. Flip and brown until no pink remains (165 degrees)

• Step 5. Top with vegetable mix; serve on gluten-free roll, bread, or wrap

PICKLED CARROTS WITH RAISIN AND DILL

Makes a great side dish for lunch or dinner

Ingredients

1 pound carrots, peeled and shredded (organic, if possible)

2 cloves minced garlic

¼ cup black raisins

¼ cup olive oil

¼ cup white wine vinegar

¼ chopped fresh dill

1 tablespoon Dijon mustard

Salt and black pepper to taste

Directions

- Step 1. Combine ingredients in mixing bowl
- Step 2. Marinate in refrigerator for 24 hours, stirring occasionally
- Step 3. Serve cold

PERFECT PICNIC POTATO SALAD

Makes 8 servings

Ingredients

1 pound red potatoes, washed and quarter-inch diced (organic, if possible)

1 cup diced celery (organic, if possible)

½ cup diced onion (organic, if possible)

¼ cup cooked, diced nitrate-free turkey or regular bacon

1 tablespoon chopped, fresh dill

1 teaspoon Dijon mustard

2 hard-boiled free-range eggs, chopped

½ cup olive-oil-based mayonnaise

½ cup full-fat sour cream

½ teaspoon salt

¼ teaspoon granulated garlic

¼ teaspoon brown black pepper

¼ teaspoon paprika

Directions

- Step 1. In a medium saucepan, boil enough water to cook potatoes until tender. Drain and cool
- Step 2. In a large mixing bowl, add potatoes, celery, onion, bacon, eggs, half of dill, salt, garlic, and black pepper; mix gently
- Step 3. Add mayonnaise, sour cream, and mustard until coated
- Step 4. Chill covered for 5 to 24 hours
- Step 5. Garnish top with remaining dill and paprika; serve cold

221

Serves 1

Ingredients

6 ounces cooked shrimp, peeled and deveined

1½ cup fresh spinach, washed (organic, if possible)

2 ounces artichoke hearts, quartered

2 ounces red onion, diced (organic, if possible)

2 ounces cooked asparagus, diced

2 ounces sliced black olives

1 clove garlic, minced

Juice of 1 lemon

¼ cup sour cream

¼ cup plain Greek yogurt, full fat

Pinch of ground black pepper

2 ounces feta cheese

Directions

• Step 1. Place spinach in large salad bowl; add artichoke, onion, asparagus, and olives. Put shrimp in center

• Step 2. In a small mixing bowl, add sour cream and yogurt; whisk

• Step 3. Add garlic and lemon juice and mix until incorporated

• Step 4. Drizzle over salad; top with pepper and feta cheese. Serve cold

Makes 6 servings

Ingredients

8 ounces cooked beef (great use of leftover steak, roast, etc.)

32 ounces all-natural reduced-sodium beef broth

½ cup diced celery (organic, if possible)

½ cup diced carrot (organic, if possible)

½ cup diced onion (organic, if possible)

1 large potato, diced (organic, if possible)

½ cup cut green beans, frozen

½ cup green peas, frozen

1 teaspoon fresh chopped parsley

1 teaspoon dried oregano

½ clove fresh minced garlic

2 ounces olive oil

Salt and pepper to taste

Directions

• Step 1. In large saucepan heated to medium high, add oil, then sauté the carrot, onion, and celery until tender

• Step 2. Add the garlic and broth; bring to boil

• Step 3. Add potato and beef. Reduce to simmer and cover. Cook until potatoes and beef are tender; add remaining ingredients

• Step 4. Simmer for 20 minutes; serve hot

FISH AND CHIP WRAP

ENZO EGGPLANT PANINI

Serves 1

Ingredients

1 4-ounce tilapia filet

2 ounces peeled shoestring (thinly) sliced potato

2 ounces egg white

2 ounces panko gluten-free bread crumbs

1 gluten free wrap (10-inch)

½ ounce lemon juice

2 ounces olive-oil-based mayonnaise

1 ounce pickled sweet relish

2 pieces green leaf lettuce, washed

1 ounce coconut oil or butter

Olive oil to coat fish

Salt and pepper to taste

Directions
- Step 1. Preheat oven to 350 degrees
- Step 2. Toss potato in coconut oil or butter, salt, and pepper. Place on greased (coconut oil or organic butter) baking sheet
- Step 3. Dip tilapia into egg white; dredge through bread crumbs
- Step 4. Arrange on greased baking sheet; salt and pepper
- Step 5. Spray with olive oil spray. Bake fish and potatoes for 15 to 20 minutes, turning fish once and potatoes occasionally until tender and brown (fish cooked to 160 degrees)
- Step 6. Mix mayonnaise, lemon juice, and relish
- Step 7. Place wrap on cutting board; add a piece of lettuce and the fish, potato, and relish sauce mix, and remaining lettuce; roll wrap; cut in half to serve

Serves 4

Ingredients

1 teaspoon of organic butter or coconut oil

1 pound eggplant, peeled and cut into half-inch slices

8 slices of large beefsteak tomatoes (½-inch thick)

8 slices of full-fat mozzarella cheese

1 tablespoon dried oregano

1 teaspoon dried basil

1 tablespoon grated Parmesan cheese

8 slices of gluten-free bread

Directions
- Step 1. Preheat oven to 425 degrees
- Step 2. Coat a baking sheet with a teaspoon of coconut oil or organic butter
- Step 3. Arrange eggplant slices on sheet pan; spray tops with vegetable spray. Bake for 12 minutes, then flip eggplant over and cook until tender to the fork
- Step 4. On each piece of bread, place slice of mozzarella cheese; add sliced tomato; sprinkle herbs and Parmesan cheese, and close slices together
- Step 5. Press or fry sandwiches for 3 minutes or until bread browns and cheese melts

Makes 1 serving

Ingredients

1 4-ounce lean, boneless pork loin, sliced thin, raw

2 ounces sauerkraut

1 ounce diced Red Delicious apple (organic, if possible)

1 ounce diced onion

1 tablespoon Dijon mustard

Pinch of ground black pepper

1 teaspoon organic butter

Pinch of caraway seeds

2 slices gluten-free bread

Directions

• Step 1. In large skillet heated to medium high, add butter and onion, and cook until browned

• Step 2. Add apple and pork. Cook until pork is tender or at 165 degrees

• Step 3. Add sauerkraut, caraway seeds, and black pepper

• Step 4. Toast gluten-free bread; spread mustard on each

• Step 5. Add pork/sauerkraut mix; serve hot

Serves 6

Ingredients

1 teaspoon of organic butter or coconut oil

2 cups boneless, skinless, chicken breast, boiled and diced

1 cup diced green pepper (organic, if possible)

1 cup diced onion (organic, if possible)

1 cup diced tomato (organic, if possible)

1 cup shredded iceberg lettuce (organic, if possible)

4-ounce can green chili pepper (drained, and chopped)

8 ounces tomato sauce

½ cup full-fat shredded cheddar cheese or Monterey Jack

1 teaspoon ground cumin

1 teaspoon chili powder

½ teaspoon ground black pepper

12 corn tacos shells

Directions

• Step 1. Coat a large skillet with a teaspoon of coconut oil or organic butter; add tomato sauce, chili peppers, chicken, cumin, chili powder, and black pepper

• Step 2. Heat on medium high until hot

• Step 3. Warm tacos shells in oven on sheet pan for three minutes at 325 degrees

• Step 4. Spoon chicken mixture evenly into shells; top with cheese, peppers, onion, lettuce, and tomato

CHICKEN SALAD WITH BROCCOLI

Serves 2

Ingredients

4 ounces boneless, skinless chicken breast

2 ounces broccoli florets (organic, if possible)

2 ounces celery, diced

1 ounce onion, diced

3 tablespoons olive-oil-based mayonnaise

1 tablespoon Dijon mustard

Salt and pepper to taste

Directions

• Step 1. Boil chicken breast until cooked. Make sure no pink shows; meat should be 165 degrees

• Step 2. Cool and dice

• Step 3. Combine ingredients; salt and pepper to taste

• Step 4. Serve on tossed salads or gluten-free bread, or use as delicious filler in stuffed tomatoes

CHICKEN CAESAR SALAD

Serves 4

Ingredients

12-ounce cooked boneless, skinless chicken breast, diced

1 head of Romaine lettuce, washed thoroughly, and cut into bite-sized pieces (organic, if possible)

2 large garlic cloves, minced

1 tablespoon fresh lemon juice

1 teaspoon anchovy paste

1 teaspoon olive-oil

½ cup olive-oil-based mayonnaise

1 tablespoon Dijon mustard

1 cup gluten-free croutons or crackers

2 tablespoon freshly grated Parmesan cheese

1 teaspoon freshly ground black pepper

Directions

• Step 1. In a medium bowl, add mayo, garlic, lemon juice, olive oil, mustard, anchovy paste, and black pepper, and whisk until incorporated

• Step 2. Divide lettuce into four bowls

• Step 3. Divide chicken into bowls, and drizzle dressing evenly. Sprinkle with Parmesan cheese; add croutons

CELERY CUCUMBER SALAD

Use as a side for lunch, dinner, etc.

Ingredients

4 ribs (stalks) celery, thinly sliced (organic, if possible)

1 English cucumber, thinly sliced (organic, if possible)

1 small red onion, thinly diced, (organic, if possible)

½ red bell pepper, seeded and thinly sliced (organic, if possible)

2 cloves minced garlic

¼ cup chopped fresh parsley

1 tablespoon Dijon mustard

2 tablespoons white vinegar

½ cup extra-virgin olive oil

Salt and ground black pepper to taste

Directions

• Step 1. In a medium bowl, mix celery, cucumber, onion, bell pepper, garlic, and parsley

• Step 2. In another small bowl, mix mustard, vinegar, salt, and pepper; slowly whisk in olive oil until dressing becomes thick

• Step 3. Toss together with vegetable mixture; refrigerate 1 hour, then serve cold

BUFFALO CHICKEN SALAD

Makes 2 servings

Ingredients

1 teaspoon of organic butter or coconut oil

4 ounces boneless, skinless chicken breast cut into even strips

2 ounces buffalo wing sauce

2 ounces bleu cheese crumble or feta cheese

1 rib (stalk) celery, washed and cut into sticks (organic, if possible)

1 small carrot peeled, cut into sticks (organic, if possible)

2 ounces diced English or burpless cucumber

2 ounces grape tomatoes (organic, if possible)

2 ounces diced red onion (organic, if possible)

8 ounces salad green, your favorite kind

Directions

• Step 1. Preheat oven to 375 degrees

• Step 2. Coat a baking sheet with coconut oil or organic butter

• Step 3. Toss chicken with buffalo sauce; arrange on baking sheet; cook for 8 minutes, then turn strips over. Cook until temperature reaches 165 degrees

• Step 4. Put lettuce in salad bowl, and top with vegetables (reserve celery and carrot)

• Step 5. Top salad with chicken; mix bleu cheese with desired dressing and top salad with dressing

• Step 6. Garnish with celery and carrot

BEEF AND BEAN BURRITO WITH SALSA

Serves 4

Ingredients

4 10-inch tortillas shells, gluten free

½ pound lean ground beef

1 15 ounce can black beans, drained and rinsed

1½ cups chopped onion

½ diced green bell pepper

1 medium tomato, seeded and diced

1 clove garlic, minced

2 ounces fresh cilantro, chopped finely

4 ounces fresh lime juice

2 ounces green chili peppers

2 teaspoons chili powder

2 teaspoons ground cumin

1 teaspoon ground black pepper

1 teaspoon salt

Directions
- Step 1. In large skillet, cook ground beef and 1 cup of onion until meat browns; drain
- Step 2. Add chili powder, cumin, salt and pepper, and black beans
- Step 3. In a medium bowl, add the remaining onion, bell pepper, tomato, garlic, chili peppers, lime juice and cilantro (mix well: this makes the salsa)
- Step 4. Spoon the beef bean mixture into the tortillas evenly; roll into burrito, and top each with salsa mixture
- Step 5. Serve with salad or Spanish rice

BARBECUE PORK BURGERS WITH CARAMELIZED ONION AND CHEDDAR CHEESE

Serves 4

Ingredients

1 pound ground lean pork

8 ounces prepared barbeque sauce (avoid the kind with high-fructose corn syrup)

1 large yellow onion, sliced

1 teaspoon coconut oil or organic butter

4 slices of cheddar cheese

Salt and pepper to taste

4 buns or bread, toasted (gluten-free)

Directions
- Step 1. Coat a large fry pan with 1 teaspoon of coconut oil or organic butter, and heat to medium high
- Step 2. Add oil or butter and onion, and cook until onion becomes brown or caramelized
- Step 3. Remove the onion from pan and hold on separate dish
- Step 4. Season pork with salt and pepper; form into four 4-ounce patties; add the pork patties; cook until brown on each side (an internal thermometer should show 165 degrees)
- Step 5. Top with cheese; cook until melted
- Step 6. Remove the patties to rolls or bread; add barbeque sauce and onion, and serve hot

Dinner

ASPARAGUS SALSA WITH CHICKEN FAJITAS

Serves 6

Ingredients

2 pounds boneless, skinless chicken breast, sliced into thin strips

1 large ripe tomato, seeded and finely diced (organic, if possible)

1 large green bell pepper, seeded and finely diced (organic, if possible)

2 scallions, diced

1 clove garlic, minced

2 tablespoons fresh lime juice

2 tablespoons olive oil

2 tablespoons cilantro, chopped

1 pound asparagus, lightly trimmed and steamed, cold-water shocked and quarter-inch diced

2 tablespoons ground cumin

2 tablespoons chili powder

1 teaspoon salt

1 teaspoon ground black pepper

Directions

•   Step 1. In a large bowl, mix tomato, green bell pepper, scallion, garlic, lime juice, 1 tablespoon olive oil, cilantro, asparagus, and salt and pepper to taste.

•   Step 2. Refrigerate for four hours or overnight.

•   Step 3. Mix sliced chicken with remaining olive oil, cumin, chili powder, salt, and pepper.

•   Step 4. In a large, coated sauté pan, heated to medium high, cook chicken, stirring frequently until chicken reaches 165 degrees internal temperature.

•   Step 5. Serve hot with gluten-free wraps or corn fajitas shells, all-natural full-fat sour cream, shredded taco cheese (organic, if possible), and refrigerated salsa.

BAKED STUFFED TURKEY BREAST

Makes 4 portions

Ingredients

1 teaspoon of organic butter or coconut oil

4-ounce boneless, skinless turkey breast tenderloin steaks, pounded thin

¼ cup diced celery (organic, if possible)

¼ cup diced onion (organic, if possible)

2 ounces fresh sage, chopped

2 ounces diced apple (organic, if possible)

½ cup cubed dried bread (gluten-free)

2 tablespoons organic butter

1 cup all-natural, low-sodium chicken broth

8 ounces all-natural or homemade turkey gravy

1 teaspoon salt and pepper

Directions

•   Step 1. In a large skillet heated to medium high, add butter, celery, onion, apple, sage, salt, and pepper to taste, and cook until tender

•   Step 2. Add chicken broth, turn heat off; add bread mix. Let moisten and cool

•   Step 3. Portion stuffing into the middle of pounded turkey steaks; fold steak over stuffing

•   Step 4. In square Pyrex dish, coated with coconut oil or butter, place turkey breast stuffing-side down; lightly coat top with olive oil

•   Step 5. Bake uncovered, 350 degrees for 20 minutes

•   Step 6. Cover breast with gravy, then cover Pyrex dish with wax paper and foil; bake another 20 minutes until internal temp reaches 165 degrees

228

BEAN AND BACON SOUP

BEEF AND BEAN SUPER NACHOS

Serves 4

Ingredients

16 ounces cooked white navy or cannellini beans, drained

1 cup diced celery (organic, if possible)

1 cup diced onion (organic, if possible)

1 cup diced carrot (organic, if possible)

8 ounces cooked nitrate-free turkey or regular bacon, diced

32 ounces all-natural, low-sodium chicken broth

2 tablespoons organic butter

2 tablespoons gluten-free amaranth flour

Salt and pepper to taste

Directions

•   Step 1. In a large saucepan heated to medium high, add butter, celery, onion, and carrot. Sauté until vegetables are soft; add flour; cook for 5 minutes, stirring constantly.

•   Step 2. Add chicken broth, stirring constantly until mixture comes to boil and thickens.

•   Step 3. Reduce heat. Add drained beans and bacon; salt and pepper to taste, simmer for 20 minutes.

This is a great winter meal you can serve with your favorite salad, vegetable, and/or gluten-free toasted bread.

Serves 4

Ingredients

1 pound lean ground beef

16 ounce bag all-natural tortilla chips (blue corn is higher in antioxidants)

1 15 ounce can black beans, drained and rinsed

1½ cups chopped onion (organic, if possible)

½ cup diced green bell pepper (organic, if possible)

½ cup tomato, seeded and diced (organic, if possible)

1 clove minced garlic

2 ounces fine chopped fresh cilantro

4 ounces fresh lime juice

2 ounces green chili peppers, finely diced

2 tablespoons chili powder

2 tablespoons ground cumin

1 teaspoon salt

1 teaspoon ground black pepper

2 cups full-fat shredded cheddar cheese (organic, if possible)

Directions

•   Step 1. In large skillet heated to medium high, brown the ground beef, then drain the fat

•   Step 2. Add black beans, 1 cup of chopped onion, the green chili peppers, chili powder, cumin, salt and pepper. Cook until onions are soft; keep warm

•   Step 3. In a small mixing bowl, add remaining chopped onion, green pepper, tomato, garlic, cilantro, and lime juice; mix well, then set aside

•   Step 4. On a large, coated cookie sheet, arrange tortilla chips, spread ground beef and black bean mixture over all the chips, add shredded cheese, and bake at 350 degrees for 10 minutes or until cheese melts

•   Step 5. Spoon the salsa mixture on top. Serve with side salad

Makes 6 servings

Ingredients

1 pound lean steak, thinly sliced

1 pound broccoli florets

½ pound sliced mushroom

½ pound red bell pepper, seeded and sliced (organic if possible)

1 8-ounce can water chestnuts, drained and sliced

3 green onions, sliced diagonally

1 clove minced garlic

2 tablespoons grated fresh ginger

¼ cup all-natural low-sodium beef stock

1 tablespoon cornstarch

2 tablespoons low-sodium soy sauce

1 tablespoon low-sodium teriyaki sauce

Directions

•   Step 1. Heat oil in wok or large skillet over high

•   Step 2. Add steak; stir for 2 minutes; add vegetables and stir another 2 minutes

•   Step 3. Whisk together beef stock, cornstarch, soy sauce, and teriyaki sauce; add to steak and vegetables

•   Step 4. Serve over quinoa or brown rice

Serves 4

Ingredients

1½ pounds flank steak, trimmed

¼ cup pearl onion

¼ cup sliced mushroom

3 ounces minced garlic

1¼ cup red wine

1 teaspoon tomato paste

¼ cup all-natural low-sodium beef broth

4 ounces ground black pepper

1 teaspoon salt

1 ounce fresh thyme

1 tablespoon organic butter

1 tablespoon gluten-free amaranth flour

Directions

•   Step 1. In a Tupperware container, add steak, 1 cup red wine, 1 ounce garlic, 2 ounces black pepper, ½ teaspoon of salt; marinate in refrigerator from 6 hours to overnight

•   Step 2. In a large skillet heated to medium high, add butter, mushrooms, remaining garlic, and onion

•   Step 3. Cook for 2 minutes; add flour and cook another 2 minutes

•   Step 4. Add red wine, beef broth, tomato paste, thyme, salt, and pepper. Cook until mixture thickens; keep warm.

•   Step 5. Heat grill to medium high; remove steak from marinade (and discard marinade); grill steak on each side for 8 to 10 minutes. Cook until done (to your liking); let cool

•   Step 6. Slice thin; arrange on large platter and top with sauce

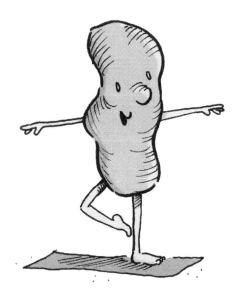

BUFFALO STEW

Serves 6

Ingredients

1 pound buffalo meat, half-inch diced

2 ounces gluten-free amaranth flour

2 ounces organic butter

1 cup of large diced celery (organic, if possible)

1 cup large diced onion (organic, if possible)

1 cup large diced carrot (organic, if possible)

1 cup half-inch cubed potatoes in cold water (organic, if possible)

2 cloves minced garlic

1 teaspoon salt

1 teaspoon ground black pepper

1 teaspoon dried oregano

1 ounce fresh thyme

1 tablespoon tomato paste

2 cups all-natural, low-sodium beef broth

Directions

• Step 1. In large Ziploc-type bag, add buffalo meat and flour; shake until well coated

• Step 2. In large saucepan heated to medium high, add butter, meat from bag; sauté until browned

• Step 3. Add beef broth and tomato paste; bring to boil, stirring constantly; reduce heat

• Step 4. Cover and simmer for 1 hour

• Step 5. Drain potatoes, and add them and the remaining ingredients to meat; cover and simmer for 1 hour or until meat is tender

• Step 6. Serve over quinoa, brown rice, or gluten-free noodles.

BUFFALO STROGANOFF

Makes 4 servings

Ingredients

1 pound buffalo meat, trimmed, half-inch diced

½ cup dry red wine

1 pound sliced mushrooms

1 cup pearl onions (organic, if possible)

1 clove minced garlic

2 cups all-natural, low-sodium beef broth

2 tablespoons organic butter

2 tablespoons gluten-free amaranth flour

8 ounces all-natural full-fat sour cream

2 ounces chopped, fresh parsley

½ teaspoon salt

½ teaspoon ground black pepper

½ teaspoon nutmeg

2 cups cooked noodles, gluten-free

Directions

• Step 1. In a large Ziploc-type bag, marinate buffalo in red wine overnight

• Step 2. In a large saucepan heated to medium high, add butter, remove buffalo from marinade (discard marinade), and brown in pan; add mushrooms; cook for 2 minutes.

• Step 3. Add flour; coat well; cook for five minutes

• Step 4. Add the onions and garlic to beef broth and stir until it thickens; reduce heat; cover and simmer 1 hour or until meat is tender

• Step 5. Stir in sour cream, nutmeg, salt, and pepper; spoon over hot, cooked noodles; garnish with parsley

CHICKEN AND PEACHES OVER QUINOA

Serves 4

Ingredients

4 4-ounce boneless, skinless chicken breasts

4 medium-firm ripe peaches, halved and pitted (organic, if possible)

½ cup quinoa, rinsed and drained

¾ cup all-natural, low-sodium chicken broth

2 ounces chopped raw walnuts

2 ounces chopped raw peanuts

2 ounces toasted raw almond slices

2 ounces diced scallions

2 ounces fresh lemon juice

6 ounces olive oil

1 sprig fresh rosemary, leaves picked

Ground black pepper to taste

1 clove minced garlic

2 ounces raw honey (local if possible)

Directions

• Step 1. Mix 2 ounces olive oil, lemon juice, garlic, rosemary leaves, and ground black pepper in glass or stainless bowl

• Step 2. Coat chicken breasts, then cover and refrigerate for 4 hours

• Step 3. Cook quinoa with chicken as directed on quinoa package; set aside to cool

• Step 4. Add almonds, scallions, 2 ounces olive oil; mix and arrange on platter, then refrigerate

• Step 5. Mix honey and remaining olive oil; brush on fleshy side of peaches

• Step 6. Heat grill to medium high, and grill peaches for 5 minutes; arrange on quinoa platter

• Step 7. Grill chicken for 8 to 10 minutes on each side or until internal temp reaches 165 degrees

• Step 8. Let cool; serve over quinoa peach platter

CHICKEN CACCIATORE

Serves 4

Ingredients

4 4-ounce boneless, skinless chicken breasts

2 ounces olive oil

2 ounces diced onion (organic, if possible)

2 ounces diced green pepper (organic, if possible)

2 ounces sliced mushroom

1 clove minced garlic

4 ounces stewed tomatoes, chopped (organic, if possible)

1 tablespoon fresh oregano, chopped

1 tablespoon fresh parsley, chopped

1 tablespoon fresh basil, chopped

½ teaspoon fresh thyme

4 ounces red wine

½ teaspoon salt

½ teaspoon ground black pepper

2 ounces Parmesan cheese

Directions

• Step 1. Heat a large skillet to medium high; add olive oil; brown chicken on both sides; remove from pan; set aside

• Step 1. In same pan add onion, green pepper, mushroom, and garlic, and sauté until tender

• Step 1. Add red wine, tomatoes, spices, herbs, and chicken. Reduce heat to simmer; cover and cook for 1 hour or until chicken reaches internal temp of 165 degrees

• Step 1. Top with Parmesan cheese

CHICKEN GYROS WITH GRILLED VEGETABLES

Makes 4 servings

Ingredients

1 pound boneless, skinless chicken breast sliced 1-inch thick

2 tablespoons extra virgin olive oil

2 tablespoon minced garlic

2 ounces chopped fresh parsley

2 ounces fresh lemon juice

2 teaspoons ground black pepper

1 teaspoon paprika

4 large wraps, gluten-free

8 ounces full-fat plain Greek yogurt

4 ounces cucumber, peeled, seeded, and finely diced

1 large eggplant sliced 1-inch thick

1 bunch asparagus, trimmed

2 red bell peppers, seeded and cut in half (organic, if possible)

Directions

• Step 1. In a small mixing bowl, mix yogurt with cucumber, 1 tablespoon garlic and an ounce of fresh parsley; cover and refrigerate

• Step 2. In another bowl, toss chicken in a tablespoon of olive oil and remaining garlic and parsley, with lemon juice, a teaspoon of black pepper and a half teaspoon of paprika

• Step 3. Coat the vegetables with remaining olive oil, black pepper, parsley, and paprika

• Step 4. Heat barbeque grill to medium high; grill vegetables for 1 minute on each side, and set aside

• Step 5. Grill chicken until thoroughly cooked, 165 degrees

• Step 6. Warm wraps quickly; fill with chicken; top with yogurt/cucumber mix; serve with grilled vegetables

CHICKEN MARGHERITA FLATBREAD PIZZAS

Makes 4 servings

Ingredients

1 teaspoon of organic butter or olive oil

2 cups boneless, skinless chicken breast: cooked, diced into ¼-inch cubes, and cooled

1 cup diced tomatoes, seeded (organic, if possible)

½ cup diced green bell pepper (organic, if possible)

½ diced onion (organic, if possible)

1 tablespoon fresh basil leaves, torn

¼ teaspoon salt

1 tablespoon Parmesan cheese

¼ cup shredded mozzarella cheese (organic, if possible)

4 plain flatbreads (gluten-free)

Directions

• Step 1. Preheat oven to 350 degrees

• Step 2. Heat a large skillet to medium high, and lightly coat with organic butter or olive oil

• Step 3. Cook onion and green pepper until soft; turn off heat; add tomatoes and salt, and mix

• Step 4. Place flatbreads on a sprayed baking sheet; arrange chicken among breads; divide tomato mix on breads; divide mozzarella and parmesan cheese on top; bake 10 to 12 minutes or until cheese is browned

• Step 5. Garnish with fresh basil; serve with side salad

GRILLED SALMON WITH ROASTED ARTICHOKES AND SPINACH

Serves 6

Ingredients

6 6-ounce salmon steaks

1½ pounds artichoke hearts

2 pounds clean, fresh spinach (organic, if possible)

6 tablespoons olive oil

1 teaspoon dried oregano

1 teaspoon dried thyme

1 teaspoon dried basil

1 teaspoon rosemary

6 cloves minced garlic

1 yellow onion (organic, if possible)

Juice of one lemon

Salt and pepper to taste

Directions

- Step 1. Preheat oven to 375 degrees
- Step 2. Toss quartered artichoke hearts in 2 tablespoons of olive oil, oregano, thyme, basil, and rosemary
- Step 3. Roast on small cookie sheet for 10 minutes. Set aside; keep warm
- Step 4. In large sauté pan on medium high, add 2 tablespoons of olive oil, onion, and garlic, and sauté until soft. Add spinach, and cook until spinach wilts; set aside
- Step 5. Heat barbeque grill, and brush the salmon steaks with remaining 2 tablespoons of olive oil, the lemon juice, and salt and pepper to taste
- Step 6. Grill for 4 minutes on each side, high heat, turning carefully
- Step 7. Top each salmon steak with spinach mixture, then top with artichoke mixture
- Step 8. Serve hot

ITALIAN FLAG PORK AND CAULIFLOWER

Serves 6

Ingredients

6 4-ounce boneless pork loin chops with the fat trimmed

3 tablespoons gluten-free amaranth flour

2 tablespoons grated Parmesan cheese

2 tablespoons fresh parsley, finely chopped

4 tablespoons olive oil

2 cloves garlic, minced

½ cup diced tomatoes (organic, if possible)

¼ cup dry, white wine

Salt and pepper to taste

1 head cauliflower, cut into florets

1 green bell pepper, seeded and sliced (organic, if possible)

1 red bell pepper, seeded and sliced (organic, if possible)

1 onion, sliced

Directions

- Step 1. Preheat oven to 350 degrees
- Step 2. Mix flour, Parmesan cheese, and parsley in a large glass or stainless-steel bowl
- Step 3. Coat pork chops
- Step 4. Heat a large skillet to medium high; add 2 ounces olive oil to skillet; brown pork chops on both sides; remove from pan; set aside
- Step 5. Add garlic, tomato, and white wine to pan; reduce heat; add browned pork chops, then salt and pepper to taste
- Step 6. Simmer, covered, for 20 minutes or until pork reaches internal temperature of 160 degrees; keep warm
- Step 7. In a large mixing bowl, add cauliflower, red and green peppers, onion, olive oil, salt, and pepper. Coat well
- Step 8. Place cauliflower mix on coated cookie sheet, and cook until cauliflower is soft
- Step 9. Serve with pork chops

ITALIAN WEDDING SOUP

Serves 6
Ingredients

1 pound lean ground beef

1 cup diced onion (organic, if possible)

2 tablespoons minced onion (organic, if possible)

1 cup diced carrot (organic, if possible)

2 ounces plain gluten-free bread crumbs

4 ounces egg whites

32 ounces all-natural low-sodium chicken broth

1 teaspoon minced garlic

1 14 ½-ounce can diced tomatoes (organic, if possible)

1 ounce fresh basil, finely chopped

1 ounce fresh oregano, finely chopped

2 teaspoons ground black pepper

6 ounces fresh spinach, washed and rough-chopped (organic, if possible)

¼ cup grated Parmesan cheese

2 ounces olive oil

Directions
- Step 1. In a large bowl, mix ground beef, minced onion, garlic, egg whites, teaspoon ground black pepper, half-ounce basil, half-ounce oregano, and bread crumbs. Form into 1-ounce meatballs
- Step 2. Into large saucepan heated medium high, add olive oil, onions, and carrots, and cook until tender
- Step 3. Add chicken broth, tomatoes, remaining basil, and oregano; bring to boil; reduce heat, and add meatballs carefully
- Step 4. Cover; cook for 20 minutes
- Step 5. Add spinach, remaining black pepper, and Parmesan cheese

NO-CRUST SEAFOOD VEGETABLE QUICHE

Makes 4 servings
Ingredients

1 teaspoon of organic butter or olive oil

4 ounces cooked cod fillets, cooled and chopped

2 ounces diced onion (organic, if possible)

4 ounces fresh spinach (organic, if possible)

2 ounces broccoli florets

2 ounces roasted red pepper, diced (organic, if possible)

2 whole eggs

1 cup unsweet almond or coconut milk

3 ounces shredded white cheddar cheese

½ teaspoon salt

½ teaspoon ground black pepper

½ teaspoon nutmeg

½ teaspoon Tabasco sauce

Directions
- Step 1. Preheat oven to 325 degrees
- Step 2. Into a heated, coated skillet, sauté onion, broccoli, spinach, and red pepper; cook until soft, then set aside to cool
- Step 3. Whisk eggs with milk; add cod, salt, pepper, nutmeg, Tabasco, and 2 ounces of cheddar cheese
- Step 4. Coat an 8-inch Pyrex dish with organic butter or coconut oil; add egg mixture; top with remaining cheddar cheese
- Step 5. Place Pyrex on cookie sheet; bake for 30 minutes or until firm
- Step 6. Cut into four wedges; serve hot or at room temperature

STIR-FRY PINEAPPLE PORK WITH BROWN RICE

Makes 4 servings

Ingredients

1 pound lean, boneless pork loin with fat trimmed, diced into quarter-inch cubes

¼ cup celery, sliced half-inch thick on bias (organic, if possible)

¼ cup scallions cut on bias

½ cup peeled carrot, sliced and cut half-inch on bias (organic, if possible)

½ cup broccoli florets

½ cup bamboo shoots or water chestnuts, canned and drained

1 cup canned pineapple chunks in own juice, drained. Reserve juice

1 teaspoon minced garlic

1 teaspoon minced fresh ginger

1 tablespoon sesame oil

1 tablespoon melted organic butter

2 tablespoons low-sodium teriyaki sauce

2 tablespoons cornstarch

1 cup all-natural, low-sodium beef broth

2 cups cooked brown rice or quinoa. Keep warm

Directions

• Step 1. Into a large skillet heated medium high, add butter and sesame oil; add pork; stir constantly

• Step 2. After 2 minutes, add celery, carrot, scallion, broccoli, bamboo shoots or water chestnuts, and cook for 2 minutes, stirring constantly

• Step 3. In a small mixing bowl, whisk beef broth, ginger, garlic, teriyaki sauce, and pineapple juice; add cornstarch; mix well

• Step 4. Add to skillet; stir until thickens

• Step 5. Reduce heat and add pineapple

• Step 6. Divide rice into four servings; spoon pork/pineapple mixture over rice

SUMMER BALSAMIC PORK AND VEGETABLE GRILL

Serves 6

Ingredients

6 pork loin chops, half-inch thick

1 large zucchini cut lengthwise one-inch thick (organic, if possible)

2 large yellow squash cut lengthwise one-inch thick (organic, if possible)

1 large eggplant cut lengthwise one-inch thick (organic, if possible)

2 red onion, peeled and sliced one-inch thick (organic, if possible)

2 green bell peppers, seeded and cut in half (organic, if possible)

2 red bell peppers, seeded and cut in half (organic, if possible)

4 ounces fresh oregano, chopped

4 ounces fresh basil, chopped

2 ounces black pepper, ground

4 ounces balsamic vinegar

6 ounces extra-virgin olive oil

Directions

• Step 1. Into a large mixing bowl, add vinegar, oregano, basil, and black pepper

• Step 2. Slowly whisk in olive oil until thickened

• Step 3. Coat vegetables in dressing

• Step 4. Heat barbeque grill to medium high; remove vegetables from dressing, draining well, and grill for 1 minute each side

• Step 5. Place on large platter

• Step 6. Toss pork in remaining dressing mix

• Step 7. Grill for 2 minutes on each side or until internal temperature reaches 148 degrees

• Step 8. Arrange pork on top of vegetable medley and serve hot

TUNA NOODLE CASSEROLE

Makes 6 servings

Ingredients

½ pound gluten-free noodles

1 pound tuna, skinned

1 cup diced onion (organic, if possible)

1 cup diced celery (organic, if possible)

1 cup diced carrot (organic, if possible)

1 cup sliced mushroom

8 ounces frozen green peas

2 cups unsweetened coconut or almond milk

¼ cup plain gluten-free bread crumbs

½ cup organic butter

¼ cup gluten-free amaranth flour

Salt and pepper to taste

Directions

• Step 1. Heat a large saucepan to medium high; add quarter-cup butter, onion, celery, carrot, and mushroom, and cook until soft

• Step 2. Add flour; stir frequently for 5 minutes

• Step 3. Add milk; stir frequently until mixture comes to a boil and thickens, then reduce heat

• Step 4. Dice tuna into quarter-inch cubes, and add to mixture; cook for 20 minutes, then remove from heat

• Step 5. Add peas, salt, and pepper, and cook noodles as directed. Drain, and add to tuna mixture. Mix thoroughly

• Step 6. Coat 2-quart casserole dish; add mixture; top evenly with bread crumbs

• Step 7. Melt remaining butter and drizzle evenly on top

• Step 8. Bake uncovered in 350-degree oven for 20 minutes or until top is brown

TURKEY MEATBALLS AND SPAGHETTI

Serves 4

Ingredients

1 pound gluten-free spaghetti, cooked

1 pound ground, raw turkey

2 egg whites

½ cup minced onion (organic, if possible)

2 cloves minced garlic

1 tablespoon dried oregano

1 teaspoon dried basil

2 tablespoons water

1 tablespoon olive oil

1 teaspoon salt

½ teaspoon ground, black pepper

1 cup gluten-free bread crumbs

4 ounces Parmesan cheese

2 ounces fresh parsley, chopped

48 ounces crushed tomatoes (organic, if possible)

Directions

• Step 1. Into large mixing bowl, add turkey, egg whites, water, onion, garlic, olive oil, oregano, basil, salt, and ground black pepper

• Step 2. Mix quickly, adding bread crumbs. Don't over-mix

• Step 3. Coat a baking pan. Arrange turkey into eight meatballs on pan

• Step 4. Bake in 350-degree oven for 20 minutes, flipping turkey halfway through

• Step 5. Into a large saucepan, add crushed tomatoes

• Step 6. Pat meatballs dry with paper towel; add to tomatoes, cook on medium for 30 minutes; reduce heat

• Step 7. Divide hot pasta into four portions; add two meatballs to each dish, and spoon sauce

• Step 8. Sprinkle Parmesan cheese and parsley on top

Exercises *for* Super Bodies

Knute Trition, Ed Yucation, and certainly X. R. Cise know the value of working one's body for peak flexibility, strength, and stamina. Because so many people are counting on you, starting with yourself, you want to keep your body in tip-top shape. Here's how: start slowly, make sure to get the form of each move right before moving on, and listen to your body. If something doesn't feel right, stop, and ask a doctor or other grown-up for help.

SQUAT

Squats work almost all your leg muscles.

- Equipment: None

How to do it: Stand with your legs hip-width apart, then ease down as though you were going to sit in a chair. Hold that at 90 degrees, then raise back up to a standing position. Don't let your knees extend beyond your toes.

- Beginner: 1 set of 10-15 reps
- Intermediate: 2 sets of 10-15 reps
- Advanced: 3 sets of 10-15 reps

Push-up

Push-ups are great for developing strength in your core and upper body.

- Equipment: Mat or carpet

How to do it: Place your hands on the floor slightly wider than shoulder-width. Your elbows should not flare out past your hands. Place your feet side by side. Maintain a straight line from your shoulders to your hips, knees, or toes — depending on which version you're doing — by keeping your tummy tight. Don't let your back sag or rise too high. Lower your body until it nearly touches the floor — hold — then rise back up to the starting position. Correct form is better than speed.

- Beginner: 10-15 reps on all fours, hinging at the hips
- Intermediate: 15-25 reps on knees, hinging at the knees
- Advanced: 25-40 reps on toes

SUPERMAN

Superman moves build up your core muscles and lower back.

- Equipment: Mat or carpet

How to do it: Lay on the floor facedown with your arms and legs fully extended. Raise your arms and legs from the hips and the shoulders, just like you're flying. Gravity will work against you. Fight it with your core muscles, and enjoy breathing calmly through it.

- Beginner: 1 set for 10-15 reps
- Intermediate: 2 sets for 10-15 reps
- Advanced: 3 sets for 10-15 reps

TRICEP DIP

Tricep dips keep the back of your arms strong and firm.

- Equipment: Chair or ledge

How to do it: Sit on the edge of the chair, scoot your bottom off, and lower then lift your body with your arms bending behind you to make a 90-degree angle.

- Beginner: 2 sets for 10-15 reps with knees bent
- Intermediate: 2 sets for 10-15 reps with legs straight on your heels
- Advanced: 3 sets for 10-15 reps with knees bent, alternating extending your right and left leg out with each rep.

CRUNCH

Crunches are easy and fun for all levels and are a solid core workout.

- Equipment: None

How to do it: Lie down on your back, both knees bent, with hands positioned beneath your lower back for support. Gently lift your head and shoulders, hold briefly, and relax back down. Don't push against your head or neck with your hands, as that can cause injury.

- Beginner: 1 set of 10-15 reps, knee bent
- Intermediate: 2 sets of 10-15 reps, floating your feet 90 degrees above your hips
- Advanced: 3 sets of 10-15 reps, extending your legs straight up so your heels point to the ceiling

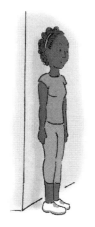

WALL SIT

You might feel a burn in your legs with this one. That means it's making you stronger.

- Equipment: Wall

How to do it: Stand up with your back against a wall, then lower down until your legs bend at a 90-degree angle. Keep your hands on your hips — and make sure your knees don't extend past your toes.

- Beginner: 1 set for 15 seconds
- Intermediate: 1 set for 30 seconds
- Advanced: 1 set for 60 seconds

240

BALL SQUEEZE

In trying to pop the ball, you'll strengthen the muscles across your chest.

- Equipment: A ball (medium or large)

Stand up, relax your shoulders, and hold a medium-sized or large bouncy ball out in front of you. Squeeze the sides of the ball together, then release slowly. Feel the muscles working across your chest on the press and release. Don't bend your elbows.

- Beginner: 1 set of 15
- Intermediate: 2 sets of 15
- Advanced: 3 sets of 15

SWIMMER

Just like a Superman, but alternate with opposing arm and leg lifts.

- Equipment: Mat or carpet

How to do it: Lay facedown and reach out ahead just as you would for a Superman. This time, lift your right arm and left leg, then lower them while raising your left arm and right leg. Do this rapidly — but always in control.

- Beginner: 1 set for 15 seconds
- Intermediate: 1 set for 30 seconds
- Advanced: 1 set for 1 minute

TOWEL BICEP CURL

You'll need a partner for this one.

- Equipment: Towel

How to do it: While standing, hold the top of your towel with hands shoulder-width apart, palms up. Your partner kneels in front of you and holds the lower ends of the towel down as you try to lift it up and down, bending at the elbows. Ask your partner to give you sufficient resistance to make this a good challenge that works the full curling range of motion.

- Beginner: 1 set of 15
- Intermediate: 2 sets of 15
- Advanced: 3 sets of 15

ROLL LIKE A BALL

Have fun — and challenge your core and balance.

- Equipment: Mat or carpet

How to do it: Sit on your bottom, hug your knees into your chest, float your feet off the floor, then roll back onto your back — hold it — then roll up back to seated position. Try not to let your feet touch the floor when you come up. Aways keep your head off the floor and look toward your belly button.

- Beginner: 1 set of 15
- Intermediate: 2 sets of 15
- Advanced: 3 sets of 15

BRIDGE

Build up your core and the back of your legs and bottom.

- Equipment: Mat or carpet

How to do it: Lie down on your back with your knees bent, hands by your side. Keep shoulders and head on the floor as you raise your hips toward the ceiling, tightening the muscles in the back of your legs and your bottom, and making a bridge shape. Make sure your knees don't go over your toes. Ease down in a controlled fashion.

- Beginner: 1 set of 15
- Intermediate: 2 sets of 15
- Advanced: 3 sets of 15, and try extending one leg up to the ceiling as you bridge, leaving the other foot on the floor

Push-up RELEASE

Build strength in your core and chest at the same time.

- Equipment: Mat or carpet

How to do it: Start out facedown on the floor in Superman form, with arms and legs floating just off the floor. Place hands and feet down, then pop up into a push-up. Lower down slowly and repeat.

- Beginner: 1 set of 15, on knees
- Intermediate: 2 sets of 15, on knees
- Advanced: 3 sets of 15, on toes

PLANK

One of the most popular core exercises, and the foundation for strengthening so much else.

- Equipment: Mat or carpet

Starting at the top of a push-up position, bend your elbows and lower yourself down until you can shift your weight from your hands to your forearms. Your body should form a straight line — like a plank of wood or a short steel beam. No arching the back or lowering the tummy.

- Beginner: 1 set for 15 seconds, from the knees
- Intermediate: 1 set for 30 seconds, from the knees or toes
- Advanced: 1 set for 60 seconds, from the toes

SIDE PLANK

Challenge your balance, strengthen your core.

- Equipment: Mat or carpet

How to do it: From the forearm as in a plank, but on your side, with your feet stacked side to side. Keep your hips raised and pushed forward. Place your non-lifting hand on your hip. Your head should stay in line with your body. For proper form, position your elbow under your shoulder.

- Beginner: 10-15 seconds, right side then left, bottom knee down
- Intermediate: 20-30 seconds, right side then left, bottom knee down
- Advanced: 30-60 seconds, right side then left, bottom knee down

SIDE TRICEP PUSH-UPS

Another great way to work the back of your arms.

- Equipment: Mat or carpet

How to do it: Lie down on your side, give your waist a hug with the arm nearest the floor and place the other hand at a 90 degree angle in front of your shoulder, and lift the top half of your body off the ground. Squeeze the back of your arm and lower back down. Hips and knees remain in contact with the floor the whole time.

- Beginner: 10 reps on right and left side
- Intermediate: 15 reps on right and left side
- Advanced: 20 reps on right and left side

SCISSOR KICKS

Feel your abdominal muscles work. This exercise will pay off big-time.

- Equipment: Mat or carpet

How to do it: lie on your back with your hands tucked under your hips. Raise your shoulders and look at your feet and belly button. Raise your feet and float them to eye level. Move your feet like scissors, over and under, side to side. Try to keep your back down.

- Beginner: 1 set for 15 seconds
- Intermediate: 1 set for 30 seconds
- Advanced: 1 set for 1 minute

POP SQUATS

Pop squats are a great way to burn fat and tone up at the same time.

- Equipment: None

How to do it: Stand with your feet together, jump out with your feet hip-width apart, and squat down carefully, as though you were sitting in a chair. Return to the starting position and repeat.

- Beginner: 1 set of 15
- Intermediate: 2 sets of 15
- Advanced: 3 sets of 15

QUICK FEET

Your heart will thank you.

- Equipment: None

How to do it: Stand with your legs hip-width apart, keep your hands out in front of your chest, and run in place as fast as you can. This is like a football drill, and it gets results.

- Beginner: 1 set for 15 seconds
- Intermediate: 1 set for 30 seconds
- Advanced: 1 set for 60 seconds

PRONE SHOULDER TOUCHES

Challenge your core and balance.

- Equipment: Mat or carpet

How to do it: Start out at the top of a push-up position, then raise one hand off the floor and touch your opposite shoulder with it. Stay up, and alternate right and left.

- Beginner: 1 set of 15, with knees down
- Intermediate: 2 sets of 15, with knees down or on toes
- Advanced: 3 sets of 15 on toes

SIDE-TO-SIDE JUMPS

Build speed to play fast and last longer.

- Equipment: String or ribbon

How to do it: Place a string on the floor as a guide. Stand along one side of the line with your feet close together and your knees soft. Jump side to side over the line as fast and gracefully as you safely can. When starting out, you can use your hands to help you stay in control.

- Beginner: 1 set for 15 seconds
- Intermediate: 1 set for 30 seconds, and try to hold your hands behind your back
- Advanced: 1 set for 60 seconds with your hands behind your back

TOE TOUCHES

Helps keep you flexible and loose.

- Equipment: None

How to do it: Stand up tall, pull in your belly button, and reach for your toes. As you rise back up, clench your bottom and keep your tummy in tight.

- Beginner: 5 slow reps
- Intermediate: 10 slow reps
- Advanced: 10 slow reps, and to challenge your balance, try to float one foot off the floor as you lower and lift

STANDING TWIST

Work your core through a full range of motion and elevate your heart rate.

- Equipment: None

How to do it: Stand with feet shoulder-width apart, knees slightly bent. Keeping shoulders down, tighten your tummy, bend the elbows slightly, and rotate torso to right until your arms are in line with your body. Rotate back through center and over to left. Continue rotating from side to side.

- Beginner: 1 set for 15 seconds
- Intermediate: 1 set for 30 seconds
- Advanced: 1 set for 60 seconds

DOWN DOG

This is a great stretch. Try to do it every day when you wake up.

- Equipment: Mat or carpet

How to do it: Start out in your incline push-up position — that's the top of a push-up position — and shift your weight back so your hips and bottom are aimed towards the ceiling. Feel the stretch in the back of your legs, calves, shoulders, and back.

- Beginner: 1 set for 15 seconds. Modify by doing this on your knees, which we call "down puppy"
- Intermediate: 1 set for 30 seconds
- Advanced: 1 set for 60 seconds

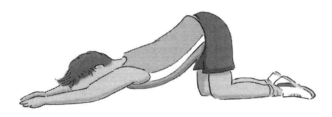

UP DOG

The opposite of down dog, and a treat any time.

- Equipment: Mat or carpet

How to do it: Start out in your incline push-up position, lower your hips and knees to the floor, keep your shoulders away from your ears, and lift your heart to the ceiling while looking up. You should feel a stretch in your hips, tummy, and chest.

- Beginner: 1 set for 15 seconds. Modify by keeping your knees down
- Intermediate: 1 set for 30 seconds
- Advanced: 1 set for 60 seconds

BUTTERFLY

This stretch is for the hips and inner thighs.

- Equipment: Mat or carpet

How to do it: Sit on your bottom, and, with the soles of your feet together, grab your ankles or toes. Take a deep breath, and make your back really straight. Lean over and aim to touch your nose to your toes. You can do it.

- Beginner: 5 slow reps
- Intermediate: 8 slow reps
- Advanced: 10 slow reps

Safety, Health, *and* Meal Planning Tips

There's no substitute for common sense, but kitchen safety is so important we want to arm you with these essential tips for getting more out of food preparation and your family's dining experience. Be safe, eat well, and enjoy.

Green Box Foods Safety Tips

Prevent food poisoning

Food poisoning occurs when you swallow food or water that contains bacteria, parasites, viruses, or toxins made by these germs. Most cases of food poisoning are from common bacteria such as staphylococcus or *E. coli*. That's why you must use different preparation surfaces for raw meats, seafood, or poultry than you would for raw vegetables, fruits, or any other food item. The bacteria in the raw proteins will contaminate the next food item.

If for some reason you can't use a new prep surface, take the time to thoroughly sanitize the one you've got before using it for something else.

Is it really clean? Is it sanitized?

To clean means to remove obvious debris. To sanitize means to free something of invisible bacteria and other pathogens. Always clean then sanitize surfaces and your hands with an approved cleaning product.

Wash your hands

It is extremely important to wash your hands frequently and thoroughly, especially after handling proteins. Use an anti-bacterial soap — and water as hot as you can stand without scalding. A good tip to ensure thorough hand washing is to wash for as long as it would take to sing the Happy Birthday song, then pat dry.

Wear gloves

Most supermarkets sell plastic food safety gloves, which are great for handling potentially dangerous bacteria-carrying foods — but they're not foolproof. Make sure you change these often when handling different foods. Gloves are not a replacement for hand washing.

You may also find gloves suitable for use in cutting in specialty chef supply stores. These metal-mesh gloves you'll wear on the hand not holding the knife, and are great protection for novice cooks and world-class chefs alike.

Avoid a can(ned good) of trouble

Never purchase canned goods if they're pierced, rusted, or dented. You might save a few pennies by buying a dented can from the discount rack, but such goods can harbor dangerous bacteria that can sicken or kill.

Knives

— Dull knives are more dangerous then sharp knives. Sharp knives go right to work; dull knives require you to work harder, apply more pressure, and risk losing control, cutting yourself.

— Always choose the right knife for the job: There's a reason stores sell such a wide variety of knives, from paring knives to cleavers. Familiarize yourself with your knife set, and always choose the right one for the job at hand.

— Never try to catch a falling knife; just back away and let it fall.

— Keep the point of the knife on the cutting board while you chop.

— Cut downward and away from your body.

— Use your free hand to hold the food item against the cutting board firmly, making sure your fingers are out of the way of potential slips.

— Clean knives immediately. When washing a knife, don't let it soak in the sink. That's only inviting someone to reach in unknowingly and risk a bad cut (and in bacterial water).

What are you cutting on?

Experts disagree on whether wood is safe to use as a cutting board, as wood can harbor food bacteria. Today, we have wood, bamboo, plastic, and glass. Each has advantages and disadvantages (some are dishwasher-safe, and some are not). Decide which cutting board best suits your needs, and cut only on a flat, even, stable surface.

Clean as you go

The sign of a smart cook is a tidy workplace. Clean as you go to enjoy cooking more, keep your work area safe and clutter-free, stay organized, reduce tension when there are children or guests around, and save time cleaning up after the meal's served.

Read like a cook

Familiarize yourself with culinary terminology when reading recipes. This will allow you to identify equipment and cooking procedures, reduce stress, waste much less, and be able to talk about cooking with kids in a way that involves them in shopping and menu planning.

Use the right tool for the right job

Modern technology has provided us with plastic, rubber, glass, and ceramic equipment. Which utensils best suit your needs? Which just waste money and storage space? Learn the best practices for your kitchen, and enjoy cooking more.

Take care when cooking with alcohol

Always remember that alcohol is flammable. When using alcohol in recipes, burn off the alcohol, and the flavor remains. Always tip the pan away from you when igniting the contents. Keep your face and hands away from the flames, and make sure you have a fire safety plan in place should things go wrong.

Know your grill

When lighting a propane grill, never put your face or hands over the surface. Never leave the cover closed when using auto ignition to light a grill. When lighting a coal grill, never pour lighting fluid on an open flame. Outside grills should never be used in enclosed spaces, as the risk of fire is great.

Avoid wild food

When getting back to nature, absolutely avoid picking foods out in the wild, unless you know exactly what you're plucking. Certain berries and mushrooms are poisonous. If you have even a vague doubt, don't take the chance. Tell kids, especially, not to eat things they find growing beyond the garden — and that you've planted in the garden — unless you've told them it's edible.

Wash your fruits and veggies

Always wash your fruits and vegetables before use, even if you're going to peel them. Take extra care when using greens and root vegetables. Wash a cut stalk of leeks and see how much sand is released.

Freezing foods

You can freeze almost any food except canned goods and shelled eggs. Some foods don't freeze well: lettuce, for example, has a high water content and molecular structure that freezing alters dramatically. Check the USDA online for charts showing how long you can safely freeze foods.

Fire safety

— Never store things on top of the stove or in the oven.
— Keep flammable items away from the stove.
— Always turn handle of pans toward the center of the stove.
— Never leave the stove unattended when cooking. If a pot should catch on fire, and it is safe to do so, turn the heat off and cover the contents with a lid.
— Never use water to extinguish a grease or electrical fire. Have a fire extinguisher close by, or use baking soda. Fire spreads rapidly, and hungrily, so if your first attempt fails and the fire worsens, don't panic: evacuate and call the fire department.

Dial in the right temperature

Make sure you have a working thermometer in the kitchen so you can take foods' accurate temperature when cooking. Calibrate dial thermometers before first use, when dropped, and monthly.

To do this, immerse the tip into ice water (32 degrees Fahrenheit) or, carefully, into boiling water (212 degrees Fahrenheit). Using a wrench, hold the hex bolt behind the dial and turn it to correct temperature. Digital thermometers have a reset button, should be tested every six months, and should have fresh batteries.

Respect the expiration date

Keep food only until it expires. When storing foods, always label and date them, e.g., macaroni salad made 9:40 a.m. on Jan. 1, 2014. Check the USDA website for a list of how long different foods can last in refrigerator, freezer or dry storage.

The temperature danger zone in which germs thrive in is 40 to 140 degrees Fahrenheit. Here are

some of the temperatures needed to keep cooked food safe:
— Roast: 145 degrees
— Fish: 45 degrees
— Pork: 160 degrees
— Ground beef: 160 degrees
— Egg dishes: 160 degrees
— Chicken breast and whole poultry: 165 degrees
— Casseroles and mixed dishes: 165 degrees

Storage

When storing foods in a refrigerator, use the drawers as they were intended. Also, never store cooked items beneath raw products, as there maybe a potential for the raw juices to drip into the cooked food. Most leftovers can be stored for three to four days. Raw products vary. Visit www.foodsafety.gov for listings of refrigerated food safety time lines.

Avoid storing, heating, and drinking out of plastic containers containing Bisphenol A (BPA), a chemical found in plastic containers and water bottles that has been found to disrupt the entire hormone system. Studies have shown that children exposed to BPA are at risk for gaining excess weight, hitting puberty too early, and increasing their risk for certain cancers and hormonal health issues.

The best way to avoid BPA is to avoid plastic as much as possible. Store and heat your food in glass containers and drink out of glass or stainless steel water bottles or cups.

Avoid Teflon

Steer clear of nonstick coatings such as Teflon (polytetrafluoroethylene, a synthetic fluoropolymer of tetrafluoroethylene you do not want to ingest or breathe) by cooking with stainless steel, glass, or ceramic pots and pans. Experienced chefs prepare superior meals by understanding how to cook without relying on chemical-coated nonstick pans.

Avoid mainstream nonstick cooking sprays

Similarly, these contain unhealthy additives such as soy lecithin, mono- and diglycerides, dimethylpolysiloxane, and dimethyl silicone. They also contain genetically modified ingredients, which are extremely high in pesticide residue. According the American Academy of Environmental Medicine, animal studies have repeatedly shown serious health risks including infertility, autoimmune disorders, diabetes, and changes in major organs including the gastrointestinal system as a result of consuming GM foods.

Healthful alternatives for cooking spray include organic butter or coconut oil, both of which have a high temperature tolerance for cooking.

Rethink soy

Soy is among the top seven common allergenic foods. Today's kids are more vulnerable to developing food allergies and the health issues that come along with allergies, such as eczema, asthma, and anaphylaxis. Soy also mimics estrogen in the body, resulting in a hormone imbalance that could contribute to weight gain and early onset of puberty and increased for serious diseases such as cancer.

Why low-fat or fat-free alternatives are not the best choices

Choosing low-fat or fat-free alternatives could be doing your family more harm than good. It's not a coincidence that our country's rates for Attention Deficit Disorder (ADD) have increased along with the "fat-free" food craze. Fat-free and low-fat food items are typically loaded with sugar or artificial ingredients such as aspartame, sucralose, dyes, and high-fructose corn syrup, all of which have been implicated in neurological disorders.

The brain is composed of more than 60 percent fat, so cutting fat out of the diet can disrupt concentration and normal appetite signals, and can promote hyperactivity and weight gain. We recommend choosing full-fat items (cheese, yogurt, etc.) to promote satiety and optimal brain development.

The benefits of going gluten- and dairy-free for kids

Gluten (a protein found in wheat) and dairy (from cow's milk) are both also high-allergy foods. They can promote inflammation in the gut, resulting in poor nutrient absorption and GI distress, typically described as "leaky gut" or "irritable bowel syndrome." Both adults and children who remove gluten and dairy from their diet notice a difference in their ability to think more clearly, and they typically have more control over weight management due to less inflammation in the body.

Meal Planning

This book is full of great recipes and nutrition tips, but we understand that meal planning for the family can be difficult. This section is designed to give you strategies to put all of those recipes and tips into action. Following a diet or nutrition plan as a single adult is fairly simple — you plan out, cook, and eat your healthy meals — but when you have a family with picky eaters or different nutritional needs, meal planning can get complicated. As a mother of five, I would like to say that I have come up with a successful meal planning system. The first thing I have found is that I have to plan out a week's worth of meals ahead of time; this is the most important strategy for success. If you plan day by day you may be wasting time and money going to the grocery store more then you need to or you may cave and get take out because you are too exhausted to think about "what's for dinner."

Follow these simple strategies and your meal planning will not be as much of a chore as it sometimes feels.

Stock up on the staples

If you are planning on eating healthy recipes with taste, then you will need to stock up on some staple items starting with herbs and spices. Go to your local farmers market or grocery store and get all of the essentials (depending on your food preferences you may add or take away from the following list, but as a base guideline this is what I recommend my clients keep stocked in their spice cabinet):

Sea salt, black pepper, garlic powder, onion powder, chili powder, paprika, cumin, rosemary, thyme, basil, oregano, chives, turmeric, curry, ginger, cinnamon, nutmeg, and dry mustard to name a few.

Staple items to have in your pantry:
All-natural chicken/beef broth, extra virgin olive oil, coconut oil, raw honey, steel cut oats, quinoa, rice, stevia, vinegars (balsamic, apple cider, etc.), all-natural nut butters like almond, cashew, or sunflower butters, raw nuts and seeds (almonds, cashews, walnuts, sunflower or pumpkin seeds).

Staples for the fridge:
Lemon, lime juice, salsa, unsweetened almond or coconut milk, eggs, and organic butter.

Make a list

Making a grocery list ensures that you will adhere to your food budget, your meal plan, and you will not forget anything. Pick a day of the week when you have a little extra time to plan out your week's worth of meal (typically a Saturday or Sunday). Start out with the simple meals, breakfast and lunch.

Breakfast

Breakfast is typically a meal that can be repeated often and should be a fairly quick process in the morning. Think about what your family would like to eat for breakfast... steel cut oats with honey, cinnamon and chopped walnuts, vegetable omelets with all-natural sausage or bacon, or smoothies.

Lunch

Lunch is also a meal that can be repeated often but tweaked slightly to avoid boredom. Salads, lettuce wraps, parfaits, sandwiches are all typical lunch options. Get your family's input on what they would like for the week in their lunch (what type of fruit, snack, and main entrée) and make your list off of their preferences.

Dinner

Dinner is probably the most complicated meal to plan because everyone is tired and hungry after a long day of school and work; they look forward to a tasty meal. Pull out recipes and plan what you are going to cook each night. This way you can pull out the meat to defrost in the morning and plan the quick recipes (crock pot or grill) for nights that are loaded with activities and the more complicated or time-consuming recipes for the nights when you are going to be home.

Snacks should be fairly simple; stock up on seasonal fruits and vegetables, hummus, raw nuts/seeds or nut butters, Greek or non-dairy coconut yogurts, hard boiled eggs, etc.

Make life easy by looking into a local food co-op or a shop from home grocery store like Green Box Foods; this will cut back on the amount of trips you have to make to the grocery store while ensuring you family is consuming high-quality certified all-natural and organic meats and fruits and vegetables.

PALA+

Here's the information we promised to help you along as you earn the Presidential Active Lifestyle Award (PALA+), formerly the Presidential Challenge Award. We've put a full flyer about it in the following pages, and you'll see there's a tracking sheet for your convenience in staying on top of your game. Fill it out, send it to Green Box Foods (our address is on the flyer), and we'll send you your certificate. Stick with the program and you'll earn an award in less than two months!

PALA+

DR. KEITH KANTOR, N.D., PH.D.

TACKLE THE PALA+ CHALLENGE INDIVIDUALLY, with a buddy, or as a family. In fact, it's best that you do take this on as a family, as families are lifelong, built-in support groups for helping everybody in them achieve amazing things.

Here's where PALA+ fits into the President's Challenge (also called Presidential Champions), a program by the President's Council on Fitness, Sports and Nutrition (formerly the President's Council on Physical Fitness and Sports):

The program encourages all Americans (international participants are also eligible) to make being active part of their everyday lives. The President's Challenge is designed to help motivate participants to improve regardless of their activity and fitness level.

The President's Challenge program includes awards for actively performing members in their preferred games, sports, or athletics.

One of our challenges will fit you or your kids' or students' lives:

— The Presidential Youth Fitness Program measures kids' and teens' physical fitness.

— The Adult Fitness Test measures an adult's aerobic fitness, muscular strength, flexibility, and other aspects of health-related fitness.

— The Presidential Active Lifestyle Award (PALA+) challenge is for people who want to make physical activity and healthy eating part of their everyday lives.

— The Presidential Champions challenge is for people who want to be more active more often.

The men and women of Green Box Foods, Inc. believe supporting youth and families in achieving attainable, measurable, and wonderful goals in sports, physical fitness, and nutrition will help them in everything they do for the rest of their lives.

With you we're shaping heroes: the next generation of Americans.

PALA+ forms and instructions can be downloaded from www.drkeithkantor.com or www.greenboxfoods.com (go to blog). While there, download Dr. Kantor's health and wellness app for iOS and Android.

Earn the *Presidential Active Lifestyle Award* (PALA+)
Formerly the Presidential Challenge Award

Green Box Foods, Inc. and our CEO, Dr. Keith Kantor, are excited to help lead the Presidential Active Lifestyle Award (PALA+) and are proud to be a PALA+ Advocate. Let Green Box Foods help your children earn the award which is also available for adults.

Simply fill out the following activity form for six (6) weeks.

For children, it is one (1) hour of activity per day and for adults, it is thirty (30) minutes per day.

For your nutritional goals simply pick one goal per week (on bottom of the attached form). They are as easy as eating smaller portions, drinking water instead of sugary drinks, or trying seafood.

If you need help planning menus or physical activities, just email us at: *dietitian@GreenBoxFoods.com* and we will be happy to help!

Once the form is complete, you can send it to us by: (1) email; just scan and email to *keith.kantor@GreenBoxFoods.com*; or (2) mail it to:

Green Box Foods, Inc.
Attn: PALA+
4355 International Blvd.
Suite 150
Norcross, GA 30093

Please fill out the following form and include it with the activity sheet when you email or mail it in.

4355 International Blvd., Suite 150 Norcross, GA 30093 p: 678-739-4800 f: 770.446.3085 GreenBoxFoods.com

257

Presidential Active Lifestyle Award
PALA+
Formerly the Presidential Challenge Award

After you and/or your child has completed the Activity Sheet,
Please complete the information below to receive a certificate
"In recognition of commitment to regular physical activity
And good nutrition in pursuit of a healthier lifestyle."

Name of Award Winner: _____

(please print clearly)

Parent's Name (if award winner is under 18 years of age):

_____

(please print clearly)

Address to mail Award Certificate to: (physical address only, no post office box please)

Street Address: _____

City: _____ State: _____ Zip Code: _____

Parent Home Phone Number: _____

Parent Cell Phone Number: _____

Parent Email Address: _____

Presidential Active Lifestyle Award: Activity + Nutrition (PALA+)

PALA+ promotes physical activity AND good nutrition, because it takes both to lead a healthy lifestyle. Sign up for the six-week program to help you maintain or improve your health. Anyone age 6 and older can earn their PALA+ today – sign up at **www.presidentschallenge.org** or use the log on the reverse side.

PHYSICAL ACTIVITY A healthy life is an active life. Youth (6-17 years old) need to be active at least 60 minutes a day (or 11,000 steps for girls and 13,000 steps for boys). Adults (18 and older), 30 minutes (or 8500 steps). So, take a walk with friends, bike ride after dinner, garden, or play a game of basketball at the park. Get your heart pumping and your muscles moving. When you've logged six weeks of physical activity, congratulations. You've started a regular routine for a more active lifestyle.

GOOD NUTRITION
Start eating healthy. It's easier than you think! Take it one step at a time. Commit to one new healthy eating goal this week, and circle it on your weekly PALA+ log. The following week add a different goal – but make sure you continue to maintain your healthy eating goal(s) from the week(s) before. Focus on your healthy eating goals every week and remember, the more often you incorporate them into your lifestyle, the better you will feel. When you've achieved six different healthy eating goals, congratulations. You've started a routine for a healthier lifestyle.

Tips for Healthy Eating:

Make half your plate fruit and vegetables.

Keep it simple by filling half your plate with fruits and vegetables at meal time. The more colorful you make your plate; the more likely you are to get the vitamins, minerals, and fiber your body needs to be healthy. Remember that all forms count – fresh, frozen, canned (fruit in water or 100% juice), dried, or 100% juice.

Make half the grains you eat whole grains.

An easy way to eat more whole grains is to switch from a refined grain food to a whole-grain food. For example, eat whole-wheat bread instead of white bread, brown rice instead of white rice, and low-fat popcorn instead of snack chips. Read the ingredients list and choose products that list a whole-grain ingredient first. Look for things like: "whole wheat," "brown rice," "bulgur," "buckwheat," "oatmeal," "rolled oats," "quinoa," or "wild rice."

Choose fat-free or low-fat (1%) milk, yogurt, or cheese.

To help build your bones and keep them strong, dairy products should be a key part of your diet because they provide calcium, vitamin D, and many other nutrients your bones need.

Drink water instead of sugary drinks.

Regular soda and other sweet drinks such as fruit drinks and energy drinks are high in calories because they have a lot of added sugar. Instead, reach for a tall glass of water. Try adding a slice of lemon, lime or watermelon or a splash of 100% juice to your glass of water if you want some flavor.

Choose lean sources of protein.

Meat, poultry, seafood, dry beans or peas, eggs, nuts, and seeds are considered part of the protein foods group. Select leaner cuts of ground beef (label says 90% lean or higher), turkey breast, or chicken breast. Grill, roast, poach, or boil meat, poultry, or seafood instead of frying. Include beans or peas in main dishes such as chili, stews, casseroles, salads, tacos, enchiladas, and burritos.

Compare sodium in foods like soup and frozen meals and choose foods with less sodium.

Read the Nutrition Facts label to compare sodium in foods like soup, bread, canned vegetables, and frozen meals – and choose the foods with lower amounts. Look for "low sodium," "reduced sodium," and "no salt added" on food packages.

Eat some seafood.

Seafood includes fish (such as salmon, tuna, and trout) and shellfish (such as crab, mussels, and oysters). Seafood has protein, minerals, and omega-3 fatty acids (heart healthy fat). Adults should try to eat at least 8 ounces a week of a variety of seafood. Children can eat smaller amounts of seafood too.

Pay attention to portion size.
Check to see what the recommended portion sizes of foods you eat look like in the bowls, plates, and glasses you use at home. For example – check 3/4 cup cereal, 3 ounces cooked chicken, 1 cup milk, 1/2 cup of juice. When dining out avoid "supersizing" your meal or buying "combo" meal deals that often include large size menu items. Choose small size items instead or ask for a "take home" bag and wrap up half of your meal to take home before you even start to eat.

If you need assistance with menu planning or physical activities, please email us at:

dietitian@GreenBoxFoods.com

PALA+
activity+nutrition

green box
F O O D S
Nutritional Wellness Benefits

www.presidentschallenge.org

Participant Name   Age   Date Started

Group ID (if applicable)   Date Completed

Week 1

Day	Physical Activities	# of Minutes or Pedometer Steps
Mon		
Tues		
Wed		
Thurs		
Fri		
Sat		
Sun		

Healthy Eating—Select a goal for this week.

Week 2

Day	Physical Activities	# of Minutes or Pedometer Steps
Mon		
Tues		
Wed		
Thurs		
Fri		
Sat		
Sun		

Healthy Eating—Circle and continue with last week's goal, and add a new goal.

Week 3

Day	Physical Activities	# of Minutes or Pedometer Steps
Mon		
Tues		
Wed		
Thurs		
Fri		
Sat		
Sun		

Healthy Eating—Circle and continue with previous goals, and add a new goal.

Week 4

Day	Physical Activities	# of Minutes or Pedometer Steps
Mon		
Tues		
Wed		
Thurs		
Fri		
Sat		
Sun		

Healthy Eating—Circle and continue with previous goals, and add a new goal.

Week 5

Day	Physical Activities	# of Minutes or Pedometer Steps
Mon		
Tues		
Wed		
Thurs		
Fri		
Sat		
Sun		

Healthy Eating—Circle and continue with previous goals, and add a new goal.

Week 6

Day	Physical Activities	# of Minutes or Pedometer Steps
Mon		
Tues		
Wed		
Thurs		
Fri		
Sat		
Sun		

Healthy Eating—Circle and continue with previous goals, and add a new goal.

Healthy Eating Goals

I made half my plate fruits and vegetables

At least half of the grains that I ate were whole grains

I chose fat-free or low fat (1%) milk, yogurt, or cheese

I drank water instead of sugary drinks

I chose lean sources of protein

I compared sodium in foods like soup and frozen meals and chose foods with less sodium

I ate seafood

I ate smaller portions

PRESIDENTIAL
ACTIVE LIFESTYLE
AWARD

A program of the President's Council on Fitness, Sports and Nutrition

Presented to   Date

*In recognition of commitment to regular physical activity
and good nutrition in pursuit of a healthier lifestyle.*

Drew Brees
Co-Chair
President's Council on Fitness, Sports and Nutrition

Dominique Dawes
Co-Chair
President's Council on Fitness, Sports and Nutrition

PALA+
activity + nutrition

261

OWN THE ART!

Not that taking care of yourself isn't its own great reward — and we're hooking you up with a certificate to show off your accomplishment — but we're going the extra mile for you, and doing it in style.

Everyone who completes the PALA+ challenge through Green Box Foods is automatically entered into a drawing to win a limited edition 12-inch by 20-inch poster of your favorite, full-color Green Box Foods comic cover!

Just indicate on your PALA+ application which of our 26 comic covers you want for your favorite wall or door (they're in the book and listed at www.drkeithkantor.com), and you just might get a poster in the mail.

We're expecting to reward lots of winners before supplies run out. Might you be among them? Good luck on your PALA+ challenge, and good luck on winning one of our awesome wall posters.

Made in the USA
San Bernardino, CA
15 September 2017